THE COUNTRY OF A THOUSAND YEARS OF PEACE

AND OTHER POEMS

THE
COUNTRY
OF A
THOUSAND
YEARS
OF PEACE

AND OTHER

POEMS BY

JAMES
MERRILL

 NEW YORK 1959

ALFRED A KNOPF

ACKNOWLEDGMENTS: "Voices from the Other World" first appeared in *The New Yorker*. Other poems are reprinted by courtesy of the following: *Botteghe Oscure, Folder, The Hudson Review, The Kenyon Review, The London Magazine, Mandrake, New World Writing, Origin, The Paris Review, Partisan Review, Poetry, Poetry London-New York, Quarterly Review of Literature, Semi-Colon, Shenandoah,* and *The Western Review.*

Eight poems were printed, five for the first time, in 1954 by Claude Fredericks at The Banyan Press, under the title SHORT STORIES. Those poems are dedicated to David Jackson.

L. C. CATALOG CARD NUMBER: 59–5432

© JAMES MERRILL, 1958.

THIS IS A BORZOI BOOK, PUBLISHED BY ALFRED A. KNOPF, INC.

FIRST EDITION

CONTENTS

THE COUNTRY OF A THOUSAND YEARS OF PEACE

AND OTHER POEMS

I

THE COUNTRY OF A THOUSAND YEARS OF PEACE

to Hans Lodeizen (1924–1950)

Here they all come to die,
Fluent therein as in a fourth tongue.
But for a young man not yet of their race
It was a madness you should lie

Blind in one eye, and fed
By the blood of a scrubbed face;
It was a madness to look down
On the toy city where

The glittering neutrality
Of clock and chocolate and lake and cloud
Made every morning somewhat
Less than you could bear;

And makes me cry aloud
At the old masters of disease
Who dangling high above you on a hair
The sword that, never falling, kills

Would coax you still back from that starry land
Under the world, which no one sees
Without a death, its finish and sharp weight
Flashing in his own hand.

There are many monsters that a glassen surface
    Restrains. And none more sinister
    Than vision asleep in the eye's tight translucence.
    Rarely it seeks now to unloose
Its diamonds. Having divined how drab a prison
    The purest mortal tissue is,
    Rarely it wakes. Unless, coaxed out by lusters
    Extraordinary, like the octopus
From the gloom of its tank half-swimming half-drifting
    Toward anything fair, a handkerchief
    Or child's face dreaming near the glass, the writher
    Advances in a godlike wreath
Of its own wrath. Chilled by such fragile reeling
    A hundred blows of a boot-heel
    Shall not quell, the dreamer wakes and hungers.
    Percussive pulses, drum or gong,
Build in his skull their loud entrancement,
    Volutions of a Hindu dance.
    His hands move clumsily in the first conventional
    Gestures of assent.
He is willing to undergo the volition and fervor
    Of many fleshlike arms, observe
    These in their holiness of indirection
    Destroy, adore, evolve, reject—
Till on glass rigid with his own seizure
    At length the sucking jewels freeze.

How unforgettably the fire that night
   Danced in its place, on air and timber fed,
   Built brightness in the eye already bright.
   Upon our knees, held by a leash of light
   Each straining shadow quietly laid its head
   As if such giving and such taking might
   Make ripe its void for substance. The fire said,

   If as I am you know me bright and warm,
   It is while matter bears, which I live by,
   For very heart the furnace of its form:
   By likeness and from likeness in my storm
   Sheltered, can all things change and changing be
   The rare bird bedded at the heart of harm.
   We listened, now at odds, now reconciled.

   I was impatient when the laughing child
   Reached for the fire and screamed. Pointless to blame
   That splendor for the poor pain of an hour.
   Yet fire thereafter was the burnt child's name
   For fear, and many ardent things became
   Such that their fire would have, could fire take fear,
   Forgot the blissful nester in its flame.

The blue wave's slumber and the rocky brow
   Almost submerged where while her father slept
   Sleep of the blue wave from his forehead leapt
   The goddess, dropped her gift, this silvery bough

   On him who among olives drowses now
   Among these drowsing boughs their trunks express,
   Pale paint from tubes so twisted, emptiness
   Might sooner have put forth the slumbering green

   Than these whose gnarled milennium bestows
   (Upon his slumber tentatively marine
   For whom endurance, lacking theirs, had been
   Too bare an ikon of the mind's repose)

   A dream, not of his dreaming, or to wean
   Roots from deep earth, rather of how each delves
   To taste infusions by whose craft ourselves,
   Once dreams in the mind of earth, like olive trees,

   Houses, the sleeper and his smile, the quais
   And tall sail bent on the blue wave, have grown
   Out of that molten center now alone
   Uneasy for its melting images.

First clan of autumn, thistleball on a stem
   Between forefinger and thumb,
   Known for the seeds
   That make a wish come true when the light last of them
   Into air blown subsides,

   Feathery sphere of seeds, frail brain
   On prickly spine,
   I feared their dissipation, deeds of this crown aspin,
   Words from a high-flown talker, pale brown
   Thistledown.

   Yet when, bewildered what to want
   Past the extravagant
   Notion of wanting, I puffed
   And the soft cluster broke and spinning went
   More channels than I knew, aloft

   In the wide air to lift its lineage
   Ha! how the Scotch flower's spendthrift
   Stars drifted down
   Many to tarn or turf, but ever a canny one
   On the stem left

To remind me of what I had wished:
That none should have clung, lest summer, thistle-bewitched,
Dry up, be done
—And the whole of desire not yet into watched
Air at a breath blown!

Of a pendulum's mildness, with her feet up
My sister lay expecting her third child.
Over the hammock's crescent spilled
Her flushed face, grazing clover and buttercup.

Her legs were troubling her, a vein had burst.
Even so, among partial fullnesses she lay
Of pecked damson, of daughters at play
Who in the shadow of the house rehearsed

Her gait, her gesture, unnatural to them,
But they would master it soon enough, grown tall
Trusting that out of themselves came all
That full grace, while she out of whom these came

Shall have thrust fullness from her, like a death.
Already, seeing the little girls listless
She righted herself in a new awkwardness.
It was not *her* life she was heavy with.

Let us each have some milk, my sister smiled
Meaning to muffle with the taste
Of unbuilt bone a striking in her breast,
For soon by what it tells the clock is stilled.

So many girls vague in the yielding orchard,
  None at my pausing but had seemed therefore
  To grow a little, to have put forth a tentative
  Frond, touch my arm and, as we went,
  Trailingly inquire, but smilingly, of the greenhouse
  —One had heard so much, was it never to be seen?
  So that it would always have appeared possible
  To be distinguished under glass
  Down ferned-faint-steaming alleys of lady-slipper,
  Camellia, browning at the fingertip,
  Yet always to find oneself, with a trace of humor,
  In perhaps the least impressive room.
  It was hotter here than elsewhere, being shadowed
  Only by bare panes overhead,
  And here the seedlings had been set to breeding
  Their small green tedium of need:
  Each plant alike, each plaintively devouring
  One form, meek sprout atremble in the glare
  Of the ideal condition. So many women
  Oval under overburdened limbs,
  And such vague needs, each witlessly becoming
  Desire, individual blossom
  Inhaled but to enhance the fiercer fading
  Of as yet nobody's beauty—Tell me (I said)
  Among these thousands which you are!
  And I will lead you backwards where the wrench

Of rifling fingers snaps the branch,
And all loves less than the proud love fastened on
Suffer themselves to be rotted clean out of conscience
By human neglect, by the naked sun,
So none shall tempt, when she is gone.

They met in loving like the hands of one
   Who having worked six days with creature and plant
   Washes his hands before the evening meal.
   Reflected in a basin out-of-doors
   The golden sky receives his hands beneath
   Its coldly wishing surface, washing them

   Of all perhaps but what of one another
   Each with its five felt perceptions holds:
   A limber warmth, fitness of palm and nail
   So long articulate in his mind before
   Plunged into happening, that all the while
   Water laps and loves the stirring hands

   His eye has leisure for the young fruit-trees
   And lowing beasts secure, since night is near,
   Pasture, lights of a distant town, and sky
   Molten, atilt, strewn on new water, sky
   In which for a last fact he dips his face
   And lifts it glistening: what dark distinct

Reflections of his features upon gold!
—Except for when each slow slight water-drop
He sensed on chin and nose accumulate,
Each tiny world of sky reversed and branches,
Fell with its pure wealth to mar the image:
World after world fallen into the sky

And still so much world left when, by the fire
With fingers clasped, he set in revolution
Certitude and chance like strong slow thumbs;
Or read from an illuminated page
Of harvest, flood, motherhood, mystery:
These waited, and would issue from his hands.

Where skies are thunderous, by a cypress walk
    Copied in snow, I have you: or
    Sitting beside the water-jet that here
    Is jet. You could be an Ethiop with hair
Powdered white as chalk

    Instead of simple diffidence on her tour
    Of monuments. Yet these first
    Images of images I shall keep.
    Once they have testified, immersed
In a mild Lethe, to what you really are,

    These insights of the mind in sleep,
    May they recall you as you never were!—
    Your charming face not lit
    But charred, as by dark beams instructing it
In all to which you were the latest heir,

    In lake, lawn, urn and maze
    Plotted by your dead rivals with no care
    That I should love you next, find milky ways
    To leave the grotto where I grieved for them.
Slowly you might have learned to bear

Estates no deed can alter. Only whim
Holds sway like gossamer
Till never breath dispels the water-wraith.
Here where no image sinks to truth
And the black sun kindles planets in noon air

The lover leads a form eclipsed, opaque,
Past a smoked-glass parterre
Towards the first ghostliness he guessed in her.
He bends her to a dazzling lake . . .
If the lens winks, it winds them who knows where.

Having used every subterfuge
    To shake you, lies, fatigue, or even that of passion,
    Now I see no way but a clean break.
    I add that I am willing to bear the guilt.

    You nod assent. Autumn turns windy, huge,
    A clear vase of dry leaves vibrating on and on.
    We sit, watching. When I next speak
    Love buries itself in me, up to the hilt.

Struck by the soft look
  Of stone in rain, wet lake,
  By the single evergreen
  Wavering deep therein,
  Reluctantly I sense
  All that the garden wants
  To have occur.
  Part of me smiles, aware
  That the stone is smiling
  Through its tears, while
  Touched by early frost
  Another part turns rust–
  Red, brittle, soon
  To be ferried down
  Past where paths end
  And the unraked sand
  Long after fall of night
  Retains a twilight.

The strange bed, whose recurrent dream we are,
Basin, and shutters guarding with their latch
The hour of arrivals, the reputed untouched Square.
Bleakly with ever fewer belongings we watch
And have never, it each time seems, so coldly before

Steeped the infant membrane of our clinging
In a strange city's clear grave acids;
Or thought how like a pledge the iron key-ring
Slid overboard, one weighty calm at Rhodes,
Down to the vats of its eventual rusting.

And letters moulting out of memory, lost
Seasons of the breast of a snowbird . . .
One morning on the pillow shall at last
Lie strands of age, and many a crease converge
Where the ambitious dreaming head has tossed

The world away and turned, and taken dwelling
Within the pillow's dense white dark, has heard
The lovers' speech from cool walls peeling
To the white bed, whose dream they were.
Bare room, forever feeling and annulling,

Bare room, bleak problem set for space,
Fold us ever and over in less identity
Than six walls hold, the oval mirror face
Showing us vacantly how to become only
Bare room, mere air, no hour and no place,

Lodging of chance, and bleak as all beginning.
We had begun perhaps to lack a starlit Square.
But now our very poverties are dissolving,
Are swallowed up, strong powders to ensure
Sleep, by a strange bed in the dark of dreaming.

II

At last through a deprived dusk we felt
　　Snow fall, white seed that would outpeople us
　　Were we not sown with many darknesses,
　　Were we not ourselves grown on the glimmering road
　　Soldiers of shade, with footholds dark in snow.
　　But as the snow ermined our passage, so
　　Of the miles beneath us, undermined and dim:
　　A wince of mole-blind noses in dense air
　　Met that cold dazzle floating down on them
　　—Of whom the slow upheavals, pain or fear,
　　Having so riddled and debased our ground,
　　Seemed now but slender hungers of a stem
　　For its right blossom. Spiraling down came
　　Billions hexagonal, unique, to kiss and crown
　　Melting, then clinging white, while, sense withdrawn,
　　Like springtime lawns under a blossomfall
　　We slept. We slept. But not by this we grew.
　　The gray snow shrank, turned hard
　　As the rich woman weary of a young man
　　Who bites his lip till it is numb with shame
　　Less for his soiling suit than her deceit
　　Nor by her grace the blood rose to a cheek
　　More pinked, more rife, a tuft of wry persistance
　　In the stunned road waking beneath his feet.

for H. I. P.

Orchards, we linger here because
  Women we love stand propped in your green prisons,
  Obedient to such justly bending laws
      Each one longs to take root,
    Lives to confess whatever season's
  Pride of blossom or endeavor's fruit
    May to her rustling boughs have risen.

    Then autumn reddens the whole mind.
  No more, she vows, the dazzle of a year
  Shall woo her from your bare cage of loud wind,
      Promise the ring and run
    To burn the altar, reappear
  With apple blossoms for the credulous one.
    Orchards, we wonder that we linger here!

    Orchards we planted, trees we shook
  To learn what you were bearing, say we stayed
  Because one winter dusk we half-mistook
      Frost on a bleakened bough
    For blossoms, and were half-afraid
  To miss the old persuasion, should we go.
    And spring did come, and discourse made

Enough of weddings to us all
That, loving her for whom the whole world grows
Fragrant and white, we linger to recall
       As down aisles of cut trees
       How a tall trunk's cross-section shows
Concentric rings, those many marriages
       That life on each live thing bestows.

Where are the horses of the sun?

Their master's green bronze hand, empty of all
But a tangle of reins, seems less to call
His horses back than to wait out their run.

To cool that havoc and restore
The temperance we had loved them for
I have implored him, child, at your behest.

Watch now, the flutings of his dress hang down
From the brave patina of breast.
His gentle eyes glass brown

Neither attend us nor the latest one
Blistered and stammering who comes to cry
Village in flames and river dry,

None to control the chariot
And to call back the killing horses none
Now that their master, eyes ashine, will not.

For watch, his eyes in the still air alone
Look shining and nowhere
Unless indeed into our own

Who are reflected there
Littler than dolls wound up by a child's fear
How tight, their postures only know.

And loosely, watch now, the reins overflow
His fist, as if once more the unsubdued
Beasts shivering and docile stood

Like us before him. Do you remember how
A small brown pony would
Nuzzle the cube of sugar from your hand?

Broken from his mild reprimand
In fire and fury hard upon the taste
Of a sweet license, even these have raced

Uncurbed in us, where fires are fanned.

In the night my great swamp-willow fell.
I had run home early, dark by five,
To find the young sphinx and the hearth swept bare
By the lazy thrashing of her tail.

A scraping on my window woke me late.
Circling those roots aghast in air
I asked of wind, of rottenness, the cause,
As yet unaware of having forgotten

Her yellow gaze unwinking, vertical pupil,
Stiff wing, dark nipple, firelit paws
—All that the odor of my hand brings back
Hiding my face, beside the boughs

Whose tall believed exuberance fallen,
Bug goes witless, liquors lack,
Profusion riddled to its core of dream
Dies, whispering names.

She only from the dead flames rose,
Sniffed once my open palm, but disdained cream,
Civilities of the aftermath.
Now even the young tree branching in that palm

Is gone, as if for having blocked a path.

During a lull at dinner the vampire frankly
Confessed herself a symbol of the inner
Adventure. An old anxiousness took hold
Like a mesmerist hissing for each of us
To call up flitterings from within,
Crags and grottos, an olive dark that lured
Casements to loosen gleamings onto the Rhine.
More fluently than water she controlled
The vista. Later, von Blon said he had known
Her expressionless face before, her raven braids
—But where? A tale . . . a mezzotint? The tone
Was that of an 1830 pianoforte.
There followed for each a real danger of falling
Into the oubliette of that bland face,
Perfectly warned of how beneath it lay
The bat's penchant for sleeping all day long
Then flying off upon the wildest tangents
With little self-preserving shrieks, also
For ghastly scenes over letters and at meals,
Not to speak of positive evil, those nightly
Drainings of one's life, the blood, the laugh,
The cries for pardon, the indifferences—
And all performed with such a virtuoso's
Detachment from say their grandmothers' experience
That men in clubs would snort incredulously
Provided one escaped to tell the story.

It was then Charles thought to wonder, peering over
The rests of venison, what on earth a vampire
Means by the inner adventure. Her retort
Is now a classic in our particular circle.

Divine uncultivation, and look, invariably
He shows up, at once lighter and darker, also
More intermittent because more independent
Than golden masses nodding in a noon breeze.
Next, barely hushing the trebled voices, he
Comes jerkily closer, see, and carries a net.
Damp, flushed, his eyes are streaming, his mouth
Shuts and opens like a ventriloquist's dummy
Eloquent with opinions it does not really believe.
Does he suffer? Yes. But you who believe that only
The mind suffers, that tears flow from its chasms,
Ought, enviously perhaps, to admit the sly
Irritant in the gold of an environment.
You might even make out some flighty flattering thing
A bit too languid and a bit too quick,
For sake of which the sufferer persists.
Remember, now that he is close enough to call,
The tears flow from his eyes, from nowhere else.
It is helpful to think of him fast in a golden fist.
Is he protected? Yes. But mischievously.

I

No wonder, shaggy saint, breast-deep in Jordan's
　　　　Reflected gliding gardens,
That you assumed their swift compulsions sacred;
Nor that, dreaming you drank, so cool the water,
Regeneration, of which the first taste maddens,
　　　　You let spill on the naked
　　　Stranger a pure and tripled mitre;

Nor that later, brooding on the sacrament
　　　　Of flowing streams, you went
Back where none flow, and went in a new dread
Of water's claspings, whose rapt robe, whose crown
Make beggar and prince alike magnificent.
　　　　A dry voice inside said,
　　　'Life is a pool in which we drown.'

Finally then, small wonder the small king,
　　　　Your captor, slavering
In a gold litter, bitten to the bone
By what shall be, pretended not to hear
His veiled wild daughter sinuous on a string
　　　　Of motives all her own
　　　Summon the executioner.

II

Our neighbors' little boy ran out to greet
   The chow, his runaway pet,
And was fearfully mauled. Breaking its mouth on fences
Down the struck street the orange mad dog tore
Until my father's pistol made of it
   Pinks, reds, a thrash of senses
  Outside the stationery store.

I was crying, but stayed on to watch. I saw
   The swelled tongue, the black maw,
And had seen earlier this meek dog trot off
Into the brambles of a vacant lot,
Suspecting then what I now know as law:
   That you can have enough
  Of human love. The chow forgot

The dim back porch, whistle and water-bowl;
   Confessing with a growl
How sweetly they subdued, forgot caresses;
Began to suffer the exactitude
Of its first nature, which was animal.
   Back in the child's oasis
  It told what it had understood.

III

The camel's vast thirst is the needle's eye.
  Whosoever faithfully
Desires desire more than its object shall
Find his right heaven, be he saint or brute.
But in a child's delirium never he
  Who next appears, the hale
    Young doctor from the Institute,

Atwirl like any exalted princess, or
  The ego of Pasteur,
Imperious for prophetic heads to probe
Upon a platter. 'Ha!' cries he, 'this brow
Swaddles a tangleworld I must explore!
  Stout vein and swaying lobe
    Redden beneath my knives. And now

'Let chattering apes, let the last proud birds screech
  Abuse, well out of reach—'
Or later, quiet, drinks in the hiss and hurl
Of burning issues down to a pronged pool
Soon parched, mere clay, whose littlest crown ableach
  Suns lighten and winds whirl
    Back into earth, the easier school.

To have a self, even of salt and sand!
  The loud, the marble-maned—at last a way
  Out of its insane frothing, those white jaws
  In which they were nothing, do you understand!

  Now that they are no longer prey to that thing,
  But for chill flushes which would come anyway
  To anyone, in moonlight or a storm,
  It is like a dream, it is past their remembering.

  Before long they have ceased to be makeshift.
  Wiry grasses keep them from blowing away,
  As does a certain creeper yearning seaward
  Over a dry admonitory drift.

  Seen from the crest, two cities catch the light
  At opposite ends of a black and white highway.
  People come out here to lose things. The dunes
  Permit themselves the first airs of a Site.

  A flowered compact, lying too deep for tears,
  Remains unsought. Yet, 'We do not give away
  Our secrets to all comers,' say the dunes
  Bridling like sphinxes at the hush of gears.

Once I think I caught them looking back.
The tide had gone far out that bright calm day
And small fish danced in death ecstatically
Upon the flashing mirror of its track.

In heaven there must be just such afternoons.
Up rose a burning couple far away.
Absolute innocence, fiery, mild. And yet
Soon even they were lost behind the dunes.

I grow old under an intensity
Of questioning looks. *Nonsense,*
I try to say, *I cannot teach you children*
How to live.—If not you, who will?
Cries one of them aloud, grasping my gilded
Frame till the world sways. *If not you, who will?*
Between their visits the table, its arrangement
Of Bible, fern and Paisley, all past change,
Does very nicely. If ever I feel curious
As to what others endure,
Across the parlor *you* provide examples,
Wide open, sunny, of everything I am
Not. You embrace a whole world without once caring
To set it in order. That takes thought. Out there
Something is being picked. The red-and-white bandannas
Go to my heart. A fine young man
Rides by on horseback. Now the door shuts. Hester
Confides in me her first unhappiness.
This much, you see, would never have been fitted
Together, but for me. Why then is it
They more and more neglect me? Late one sleepless
Midsummer night I strained to keep
Five tapers from your breathing. *No,* the widowed
Cousin said, *let them go out.* I did.
The room brimmed with gray sound, all the instreaming
Muslin of your dream . . .

Years later now, two of the grown grandchildren
Sit with novels face-down on the sill,
Content to muse upon your tall transparence,
Your clouds, brown fields, persimmon far
And cypress near. One speaks. *How superficial
Appearances are!* Since then, as if a fish
Had broken the perfect silver of my reflectiveness,
I have lapses. I suspect
Looks from behind, where nothing is, cool gazes
Through the blind flaws of my mind. As days,
As decades lengthen, this vision
Spreads and blackens. I do not know whose it is,
But I think it watches for my last silver
To blister, flake, float leaf by life, each milling–
Downward dumb conceit, to a standstill
From which not even you strike any brilliant
Chord in me, and to a faceless will,
Echo of mine, I am amenable.

III

'Au pays qui te ressemble'

There is a city whose fair houses wizen
    In a strict web of streets, of waterways
    In which the clock tower gurgles and sways,
    And there desire is freed from the body's prison.

    Into a black impasse deep in the maze
    A mirror thrusts her brilliant severed head,
    Mouth red and moist, and pale curls diamonded.
    A youth advances towards the wraith, delays,

    Squints through the window at a rumpled bed,
    Cat, the familiar, lolling on batik,
    The leman's person now no more unique
    Than any hovel uninhabited,

    Then turns, leaving her wrappered in a reek
    Of realism, back the way he came.
    Her jewels rekindle in their sooty frame
    Lights for a future sleuth of the oblique.

    (Once, once only to have laid absolute claim
    Upon that love long held in readiness,
    Not by the flesh in any stale undress,
    Nor by the faithful ghost whose lips inflame

Lips curling dry, licked once to evanesce;
One night one autumn, so to have taken hold
Of certain volumes violent yet controlled
As to leave nothing for regret, unless

A strand of hair, pale auburn not quite gold
On the creased cushion, being what you must bear,
Guided the passion to its hush, like prayer,
And paler, cooler, tapered, as foretold,

Into the sheer gold of nobody's hair,
The fragrance of whatever we suppose
Wafted, as music over water flows
Into the darkened sleeper, now elsewhere . . .)

Next day, is it myself whose image those
Sunning their own on the canal's far side
Are smiling to see reel at the downglide
Of one leaf, wallow, painfully recompose?

My head has fallen forward open-eyed.
Word of somebody's Schumann—'like a swan
That breasts a torrent of obsidian'—
Idles below me in formaldehyde.

Have I become my senses, all else gone?
A warm gust from the luxurious act
Interrupts reflection, leaves it tracked
With dust, like water sunlight moves upon.

By dark the world is once again intact,
Or so the mirrors, wiped clean, try to reason . . .
O little moons, misshapen but arisen
To blind with the emotions they refract!

Charles used to watch Naomi, taking heart
  And a steel saw, open up turtles, live.
  While she swore they felt nothing, he would gag
  At blood, at the blind twitching, even after
  The murky dawn of entrails cleared, revealing
  Contours he knew, egg-yellows like lamps paling.

  Well then. She carried off the beating heart
  To the kymograph and rigged it there, a rag
  In fitful wind, now made to strain, now stopped
  By her solutions tonic or malign
  Alternately in which it would be steeped.
  What the heart bore, she noted on a chart,

  For work did not stop only with the heart.
  He thought of certain human hearts, their climb
  Through violence into exquisite disciplines
  Of which, as it now appeared, they all expired.
  Soon she would fetch another and start over,
  Easy in the presence of her lover.

I. WATER BOILING

When Polly's reddening hand
　　Let fall into the kettle
　　The greenest few of all
　　Her backyard's victuals

　　Which early underground
　　Imbibed from the hot metals
　　A cooking lacking little
　　To set them on her table

　　How while each knowing bubble
　　Jolted ebulliently
　　Good it felt to be going
　　At last where the ideal

　　Erupting of an eyeball
　　That dwelt more than its fill
　　On summer's flame shall scour
　　The kitchen from the hill!

2. NIGHT LAUNDRY

Of daily soilure laving
Fabric of all and sundry
With no time for believing
Loving might work the wonder

Who among clouded linen
Has scattered blueing then
Well over wrist in grieving
Dismissed all but the doing

May see to clotheslines later
A week of swans depending
From wooden beaks take flight
Flapping at dawn from water's

Jewel of the first water
And every dismal matter's
Absorption in its cleansing
Bring the new day to light.

3. ITALIAN LESSON

It will not do Luigi
You in this fireless room
Tirelessly expounding
The sense of so much sound

As if to speak were rather
Those promenades in Rome
Where each cool eye plays moth
To flames largely its own

Than the resounding Latin
Catacomb or labyrinth
Corinthian overgrown
With French sphinx or the heated tones

Of all these quenched at nightfall
Yet sparkling on a lip
At whose mute call I turn
To certain other lessons hard to learn.

Poor little Agnes cried when she saw the iceberg.
  We smiled and went on with our talk, careless
  Of its brilliant fraction and, watchful beneath,
  That law of which nine-tenths is a possession
  By powers we do not ourselves possess.
  Some cold tide nudged us into sunny gales
  With our money and our medications. No,
  Later in shops I thought again of the iceberg.
  Mild faces turned aside to let us fondle
  Monsters in crystal, tame and small, fawning
  On lengths of ocean-green brocade.
  'These once were nightmares,' the Professor said,
  'That set aswirl the mind of China. Now
  They are belittled, to whom craftsmen fed
  The drug of Form, their fingers cold with dread,
  Famine and Pestilence, into souvenirs.'
  'Well I'm *still* famished,' said a woman in red
  Whose name escapes me now. I wondered then:
  Are we less monstrous when our motive slumbers
  Drugged by a perfection of our form?
  The bargain struck, a thin child parted curtains.
  We took to lunch our monsters wrapped in silk.
  They have become our own. Beneath them stretch
  Dim shelves adrowse, our hungers and the dread
  That, civilizing into cunning shapes,
  Briefly appeased what it could not oppose.

45

I. THE TOURIST

Now Henry (said his Aunt) take care.
She may not realize who you are.
And if her speech is less than lucid
Try to remember always that in
Her day she spoke, not counting Latin,
Nine languages. Think what she did,
Or meant to do, before the war.
Was there anyone like her?

Palermo lay at her feet. Madrid
Trembled, a moonstone from her ear.
Avoid all mention of your Grandfather.
Poor soul, she's peevish now, an invalid,
Has lost her beauty, gets things wrong.
Go now. But do not stay too long.

2. GEOGRAPHY

The white bull chased her. Others said
All interest vanished. Anyhow, she fled,

Her mantle's flowing border torn
To islands by the Golden Horn,

Knee bared, head high, but soon to set
One salty cheek on water, let

Flesh become grass and high heart stone,
And all her radiant passage known

Lamely as Time by some she dreamt not of.
Who come to pray remain to scoff

At tattered bulls on shut church doors
In black towns numberless as pores,

The god at last indifferent
And she no longer chaste but continent.

3. AT THE BULLFIGHT

Deep in the gaunt mask arenas blaze.
To creaking music now appear
Champions of her honor, with fixed gaze
And slow parading through a maze
Where the thing waits. Just once in fear
She stiffens, wonders that her people cheer
Pelting down roses and berets.
Then on the mask a smile plays, absent, queer.

In a fringed shawl of blood the bull
Moans and kneels down. His huge eye glazes
On the confusing candor of her gauzes
Who called, who of her own young will
Hung him with garlands, tickled his nostril
And urged him into the foam with gentle phrases.

Righteous or not, here comes an angry man
     Done up in crimson, his face blackened
     If only by the smoke of a self-purifying flame.
     Now he is thrusting his hand into the flame
     To sear away not, as he said, a moment's folly
     So much as his hand, the useful part of it.
     I must confess this fails, after a bit,
     To produce the intended effect on us.
     We had loved each other freely, humanly
     With our own angers and our own forgiveness
     —Who now, made light of by his seriousness,
     Gases on which flame feeds, are wafted up
     With lyre and dart, public, hilarious,
     Two cupids cuddling in a cupola.
     Useless to say he is acting for our sakes.
     One does not care for those who care for one
     More than one cares for oneself. Divine or not,
     At the end he calls upon justice. But, my dear,
     Little shall startle from the embers, merely
     A grinning head incensed, a succulence
     On which to feast, grinning ourselves, I fear.

I used to write in the café sometimes:
Poems on menus, read all over town
Or talked out before ever written down.
One day a girl brought in his latest book.
I opened it—stiff rhythms, gorgeous rhymes—
And made a face. Then crash! my cup upset.
Of twenty upward looks mine only met
His, that gold archaic lion's look

Wherein I saw my wiry person skinned
Of every skill it labored to acquire
And heard the plucked nerve's elemental twang.
They found me dangling where his golden wind
Inflicted so much music on the lyre
That no one could have told you what he sang.

Ah downward through the dark coulisse,
  Impelled to walk the stage of hell,
  Unwind as in a theater gilt and puce
  His opulence of pain until

  Each damned soul dropped its trembling fan
  (Which in the gusts of wooing trembled still)
  And wept to hear him: it was then
  Sickeningly he divined, but with an odd thrill,

  Among the shadows of a box
  That brow, that hand outspread upon
  The plush worn bare, a white peacock's
  Genius at dusk on a dissolving lawn,

  Her loss within his music's rise and fall
  Having become perpetual.

Most recent in the long race that descends
From me, welcome! and least askew of ikons
That grow on a new page like rapid lichens
Among the telephone numbers of new friends.

These I commune with every day. Hellos,
Goodbyes. Often by dusk a pair of eyes
Is all I draw; the pencil stupefies
Their lids with kohl until they almost close

But then do not, as if, more animate
Than any new friend's voice flattened by news,
Guessing some brilliant function I refuse,
And why, and wanting to accept their fate.

Noses as yet, alas, revert to profile.
Lips, too, are pursed in this or that direction,
Or raised to other lips from sheer distraction;
To mine, not once. While still, just as at Deauville

Off-season, tiny hands are better hidden
By great muffs of albino porcupine.
Indeed, nothing I do is at all fine
Save certain abstract forms. These come unbidden:

Stars, oblongs linked, or a baroque motif
Expressed so forcibly that it indents
A blank horizon generations hence
With signs and pressures, massing to relief

Like thunderheads one day in sultry foretaste
Of flashes first envisioned as your own
When, squat and breathless, you inscribe on stone
Your names for me, my inkling of an artist—

He-Who-endures-the-disembodied-Voice
Or *Who-in-wrath-puts-down-the-Black-Receiver*—
And, more than image then, a rain, a river
Of prescience, you reflect and I rejoice!

Far, far behind already is that aeon
Of pin-heads, bodies each a ragged weevil,
Slit-mouthed and spider-leggèd, with eyes like gravel,
Wavering under trees of purple crayon.

Shapes never realized, were you dogs or chairs?
That page is brittle now, if not long burned.
This morning's little boy stands (I have learned
To do feet) gazing down a flight of stairs.

And when A. calls to tell me he enjoyed
The evening, I begin again. Again
Emerge, O sunbursts, garlands, creatures, men,
Ever more lifelike out of the white void!

IV

Ticklish no longer
  With tangibility
  Nor rooted, crimson, over
  The worm's inching stupor

  Little but a spirit
  Costly and volatile
  Am I, want of my touch unstoppers
  Now that you suffer it.

Now each has climbed to the uninhabitable
My song rings oddly. Soot floats down the street.
Behind plate glass rot sweets no one shall eat,
While overhead on its iron grill
Somebody's shape a sheet
Unwinds from slowly tosses in our moonless heat.

Those others, who knows where they are?
The lonely man. He steals through doors ajar
Up to some breathing pen
Of brothers, pours a phial of his own pain
Into each sleeper's ear, then slips unseen
Down towards day, the happy din.

The sleeper knows. Rivers inside of him
Rise. His palms glide upon his own dark skin.
His eyes sleep-blind but gleaming wide
Fill with the same warm tide
That laps our piers come morning. In his dream
The highest water mark stands for wisdom.

I, I know only that when the dawn mist
Discourages one bare gold dome like rust,
When stones fume I shall rest,
Loving my neighbor as I love myself,
No more, no less, for I do not love myself . . .
But something stirs, stirs now. At love's name? No,

No apparition, neither any abrupt gust
Of roses' fragrance, here where none grow:
The hair rises almost,
The throat just tries to close, so quietly do
You find me, topple at my feet, poor ghost,
Sung to sleep by a first and faraway cockcrow.

You I forget, you whom the immemorial
Wraps round with many a foolish vow,
Hush! all at once our graying prospects billow
Like cloths, a canvas town.
My eyes fill with a seeing not their own.
Those cloths aside, your sleep is what I know.

I have forgotten how. I try to wake,
I want to. But an eye, when morning comes,
Weeps grains of sand, an ear a bitter wax,
The linen winds and wrinkles like shed skin.

Outside, the angel fumbles with a rake.
He has forgotten, too. And by fall, albums
Are full of studies done in browns and blacks
For one stilled figure, rarely a face drawn in.

Father, your blind hound fleetest when he lies
In the familiar dream of weapon and flight
Stirring, will puzzle at my outstretched palm,

Then let me merge into those images
Whose odors guide, that can no more excite,
His silvering muzzle towards your perfect calm.

But in the end one tires of the high-flown.
If it were simply a matter of life or death
We should by now welcome the darkening room,
Wrinkling of linen, window at last violet,
The rosy body lax in a chair of words,
And then the appearance of unsuspected lights.
We should walk wonderingly into that other world
With its red signs pulsing and long lit lanes.
But often at nightfall, ambiguous
As the city itself, a giant jeweled bird
Comes cawing to the sill, dispersing thought
Like a bird-bath, and with such final barbarity
As to wear thin at once terror and novelty.
So that a sumptuous monotony
Sets in, a pendulum of amethysts
In the shape of a bird, keyed up for ever fiercer
Flights between ardor and ashes, back and forth;
Caught in whose talons any proof of grace,
Even your face, particularly your face
Fades, featureless in flame, or wan, a fading
Tintype of some cooling love, according
To the creature's whim. And in the end, despite
Its pyrotechnic curiosity, the process
Palls. One night
Your body winces grayly from its chair,
Embarks, a tearful child, to rest

On the dark breast of the fulfilled past.
The first sleep here is the sleep fraught
As never before with densities, plume, oak,
Black water, a blind flapping. And you wake
Unburdened, look about for friends—but O
Could not even the underworld forego
The publishing of omens, naively?
Nothing requires you to make sense of them
And yet you shiver from the dim clay shore,
Gazing. There in the lake, four rows of stilts
Rise, a first trace of culture, shy at dawn
Though blackened as if forces long confined
Had smouldered and blazed forth. In the museum
You draw back lest the relics of those days
—A battered egg cup and a boat with feet—
Have lost their glamour. They have not. The guide
Fairly exudes his tale of godless hordes
Sweeping like clockwork over Switzerland,
Till what had been your very blood ticks out
Voluptuous homilies. Ah, how well one might,
If it were less than a matter of life or death,
Traffic in priceless jewels, 'live' and 'die'!
But couldn't the point about the phoenix
Be not agony or resurrection, rather
A mortal lull that followed either,
During which flames expired as they should,
And dawn, discovering ashes not yet stirred,
Buildings in rain, but set on rock,
Beggar and sparrow entertaining one another,

Showed me your face, for that moment neither
Alive nor dead, but turned in sleep
Away from whatever waited to be endured?

Presently at our touch the teacup stirred,
Then circled lazily about
From A to Z. The first voice heard
(If they are voices, these mute spellers-out)
Was that of an engineer

Originally from Cologne.
Dead in his 22nd year
Of cholera in Cairo, he had 'known
No happiness.' He once met Goethe, though.
Goethe had told him: *Persevere*.

Our blind hound whined. With that, a horde
Of voices gathered above the Ouija board,
Some childish and, you might say, blurred
By sleep; one little boy
Named Will, reluctant possibly in a ruff

Like a large-lidded page out of El Greco, pulled
Back the arras for that next voice,
Cold and portentous: 'All is lost.
Flee this house. Otto von Thurn und Taxis.
Obey. You have no choice.'

Frightened, we stopped; but tossed
Till sunrise striped the rumpled sheets with gold.
Each night since then, the moon waxes,
Small insects flit round a cold torch
We light, that sends them pattering to the porch ...

But no real Sign. New voices come,
Dictate addresses, begging us to write;
Some warn of lives misspent, and all of doom
In ways that so exhilarate
We are sleeping sound of late.

Last night the teacup shattered in a rage.
Indeed, we have grown nonchalant
Towards the other world. In the gloom here,
Our elbows on the cleared
Table, we talk and smoke, pleased to be stirred

Rather by buzzings in the jasmine, by the drone
Of our own voices and poor blind Rover's wheeze,
Than by those clamoring overhead,
Obsessed or piteous, for a commitment
We still have wit to postpone

Because, once looked at lit
By the cold reflections of the dead
Risen extinct but irresistible,
Our lives have never seemed more full, more real,
Nor the full moon more quick to chill.

The site relives its tender monotone
  In the begging children's bodies, thin and dark.
  They even sleep here, watched over by a far dog's bark
  Setting its faint pockmark onto the stone

  Up out of which, every morning, small temples have grown
  Like organs, those that nourish or beget,
  At the onset of a pubescence yet
  More longed-for and more alien than our own.

Softening the marbles, day
   Is dawning, which two elms vein.
   Presently, slow as crochet,
   White veils grow across the scene.
   Now that my life has lost its way
   I watch for it, through a cold pane

   Out past all this eloquence
   Inside: look, gesture, flowing raiment
   Done in porphyry or jasper whence
   One white arm, for a long moment
   Raised to strike, relents
   (Not to spoil one's enjoyment)

   Back into stone, back into being
   Hard, handsome to the fingertips,
   With eyes that bulge unseeing
   To call down an immaculate eclipse
   Upon the world. It began snowing
   Because of the statues, perhaps.

Or because for a long time now
I have wanted to be more natural
Than they, to issue forth anew
In a profusion inimitable
As it is chaste and quickly through.
White void, my heart grows full

With all you have undone!
Starwise, from coldest heights, a gong
Of silence strikes *end of an aeon*,
Reverberates keen and strong
Until a far veil lifts. Someone
Is stumbling this way. Neither young

Nor old, man nor woman, so
Propelled by cold, a human figure
Barely begun, a beggar, no,
Two by now, and ever nearer, bigger,
Cause me to stiffen in a show
Of being human also, eager

For what never, never occurs.
In the tradition of their kind
Exhaustingly the wayfarers
Breathe out white and pass by blind.
After them trot two ermine-yellow curs.
These look up, almost lag behind,

Then follow with two unheard shakes
Of bells. As my eyes close, nearby
Something unwinds and breaks.
Perhaps the Discus Thrower has let fly
Or Laocoön stepped from his snakes
Like old clothes. The scene changes. I

Am mounted in a village common.
A child calls. Early lamps and sunset
Stream together down the snowman's
Face and dazzle in his jet
Eyes. He lives, but melts. I summon
All my strength. I wake in a cold sweat.

You are beside me. It is dawn
In a friend's house in late
Summer. I softly rise, put on
A robe, and by the misty light
Watch you sleep. You moan
Once in your own dream, and are quiet.

I turn to look outdoors
At the formal garden our friend made.
A figure kneels among the flowers,
A limestone river-god,
Arm raised so that a clear stream pours
From the urn level with his head.

But a white, eyeless shape
Is gesturing deep in my dream.
I turn back to you for companionship.
At once there rises like perfume
To numb me, from your too heavy sleep,
What we said last night in this room—

All of it muffled to protect
Our sleeping friend—when for a wild
Half-hour the light burned, the clock ticked.
You called me cold, I said you were a child.
I said we must respect
Each other's solitude. You smiled.

Well, I shall wake you now,
Smiling myself to hide my fear.
Sun turns the stone urn's overflow
To fire. If I had missed before
The relevance of the road in snow,
The little dogs, the blinded pair,

I judge it now in your slow eyes
Which meet mine, fill with things
We do not name, then fill with the sunrise
And close, because too much light stings,
All the more when shed on these
Our sleeps of stone, our wakenings.

I

To a head at daybreak
Abolishing its dreams
No use naming the forms
Numbed in one small rock

Which, for it understands
That blind necessity
Neither to suffer, grow nor die,
Hangs heavy on my hands.

II

Now just the least part of you
Can be reached by love, as when
The world coming between
Causes a crescent moon.

III

O to have traveled
Far in the oblong emerald,
Learned how to endure
Thresholds diminishing
To a green vanishing . . .
How small and pure
We should have turned
Before our journey's end.

The plain dries outward from its heart.
The wise flat-bottomed clouds depart
With all their secrets. Green and gold
The land still tries to look controlled
But one leaf panics. It will start

Now. A chirring numbs the air.
Live shrouds abruptly from nowhere
Fill up the failing streams like dirt.
Each tree puts on a dull brown shirt
And slumps, bowed down with care.

You think first: This is no rain
Of locusts, rather my own brain
At work, whose preconceptions dye
The whole world drab. Or bluntly: I
Am dreaming, or insane.

The next day dawns upon no dream.
There is wide evidence of Them,
Such as the myriad dead or maimed
In furrows, in that yet unnamed
Trickle of corpses, once a stream.

Step gingerly; for they were real,
The locusts, after all.
Wearing opaque goggles (proof
Of a vestigial inner life?)
They have the dead hue of the useful,

The weak husk of no great event.
You feel nothing. It is time you went
Back to where everything was clear,
Where trouble was a limpid source to peer
Deep into, heaven-sent

Mirrorscope, green, wet,
All echo, orchid, and egret
In pure transports recalling you.
Go. A young man before you do
Is apt to roll a cigarette

And talk. Come spring (he says)
The grubs will hatch from crevices
To eat up anything that may have bloomed.
How strange, with all of it foredoomed,
His caring for that scant green is!

What can be said to him? The glue
Of dead wings thickens on your shoe.
Indeed, only when far behind
Does the experience make a kind
Of weird sense. One night over the bayou

Certain great clouds you have seen before
Move in, give way to a downpour.
They have been told at last, it seems,
About the flayed trees and the choked streams.
Rain wakes you, pounding on the door.

The parquet barely gleams, a lake.
  The windows weaken the dark trees.
  The mirrors to their bosoms take
  Far glints of water, which they freeze
  And wear like necklaces.

  Some pause in front of others with
  Glimmers of mutual admiration.
  Even to draw breath is uncouth.
  Steps make the silver marrow spin
  Up and down every spine.

  You feel that something must begin.
  To clickings from the chandeliers
  A woman and a man come in
  And creak about. She sighs, he peers.
  A guide hisses in their ears,

  'Your seeresses of sheer Space
  In argent colloquy despise
  Anything personal or commonplace.'
  Looked at, the mirrors close their eyes.
  Through the guide's good offices

In one glass brow a tree is lit
That multiplies itself in tiers,
Tempting the pair to populate
Those vistas from which visitors
Ricochet in fours,

Eights, sixteens, till the first two gaze
At one another through a glazed crush
Of their own kind, and the man says,
'Complex but unmysterious,
This is no life for us.'

He shuts the camera whose cold eye
Far outshone his own or hers.
The woman, making no reply,
Scans the remotest mirrors within mirrors
For grander figures,

Not just those of herself and him
Repeated soothingly, as though
Somebody's wits were growing dim—
Those! those beyond! The guide says, 'Time to go.'
They turn to do so,

And of a million likenesses
The two had thought to leave behind
Not one but nimble as you please
Turns with them, masterfully aligned.
Then all slip out of mind

And in the solitary hall
The lobes of crystal gather dust.
From glass to glass an interval
Widens like moonrise over frost
No tracks have ever crossed.

Hans, there are moments when the whole mind
    Resolves into a pair of brimming eyes, or lips
    Parting to drink from the deep spring of a death
    That freshness they do not yet need to understand.
    These are the moments, if ever, an angel steps
    Into the mind, as kings into the dress
    Of a poor goatherd, for their acts of charity.
    There are moments when speech is but a mouth pressed
    Lightly and humbly against the angel's hand.

James Merrill was born in New York in 1926. He attended Lawrenceville School and was graduated from Amherst College in 1947, having meanwhile served for one year as an infantry private. He has taught literature and creative writing at Bard College and Amherst. His First Poems appeared in 1951. A play in prose, The Immortal Husband, received an off-Broadway production in 1955 and was included in Playbook (1956). The Seraglio, his first novel, was published in 1957. Mr. Merrill lives in Stonington, Connecticut.

The text of this book was set on the Monotype in a face called BEMBO. The roman is a modern revival of a letter cut for Aldus Manutius of Venice, by Francesco Griffo, in 1495. The italic is an adaptation of a chancery script type of the early sixteenth century cut by Lodovico degli Arrighi of Rome. The type is named for Cardinal Pietro Bembo, in whose book De Aetna, published in 1495, it was first used.

The book was composed and printed by CLARKE & WAY, at THE THISTLE PRESS, New York; paper manufactured by S. D. WARREN COMPANY, Boston; bound by H. WOLFF, New York; designed by HARRY FORD.

JARANO

The Texas Pan American Series

JARANO

BY RAMÓN BETETA

Translated from the Spanish by JOHN UPTON

PROLOGUE BY SALVADOR NOVO

Drawings by Mario Pérez O.

UNIVERSITY OF TEXAS PRESS, AUSTIN & LONDON

114807

The Texas Pan American Series is published with
the assistance of a revolving publication fund established by the Pan American Sulphur Company and
other friends of Latin America in Texas.

International Standard Book Number 0–292–70036–9
Library of Congress Catalog Card Number 75–121124
Printed by The University of Texas Printing Division, Austin
Bound by Universal Bookbindery, Inc., San Antonio

P R O L O G U E

On October 5, 1965, a day like any other, we heard the staggering news: Ramón Beteta had died at his home, suddenly, in a matter of minutes.

He had worked late that day at the newspaper of which he was editor, and then had dictated to his secretary another in his series of television talks. These were comments on current events, reminiscent of his former lectures at the University, and occasionally included an interview with some distinguished visitor. His programs had all the easy informality of an after-hours chat with his colleagues at the paper, as though he were leaning back in his chair in his shirt sleeves, legs stretched out before him.

The small book the reader holds in his hand was unpublished and possibly unfinished at his untimely death.

He had by no means reached that serene and sterile age when men are given to writing their memoirs, as a kind of final burst of activity. He was in his full, productive maturity.

Ramón Beteta had served his country in many ways. He had been a university professor; he had held posts both in what was later to become the Department of Health and Welfare and in the Department of Education, where he soon gained a thorough knowledge of the problems and economic importance of the In-

dian population; he had served on the board of directors of the
National Railways; he had been Secretary of the Treasury; and,
finally, as director of Miguel Alemán's political campaign he had
brought his wealth of experience to the shaping of the economic
structure that was soon to result in Mexico's industrial development and sound financial position.

He had served as ambassador to Italy and Greece, where—
perennial student that he was—he had rounded out an already
mature intelligence with broadened cultural horizons and new
concepts; then he had returned to bestow this wealth upon his
country from the rostrum of an honest newspaper.

There was no branch of the arts that he did not respect and
encourage: symphonic music, the theater, painting. Beneath the
economist, the financier, and the professor were the artist, the
writer, and even the amateur watercolorist, sharing with his
brother the pleasure of rendering the spectacle of life in form and
color.

Even though, as I have said, he had not reached that age when
men are ready to write their memoirs, he has done so to some
extent in the chapters dealing with his childhood—those dramatic
glimpses of pre-Revolutionary Mexico at the beginning of this
century.

In earlier books he had displayed the lucid, solid maturity of
his social and political thought. There Ramón Beteta had projected himself outward, toward others; in this volume he takes
up with equal frankness and sincerity the exploration of his own
personality, delving to the roots of childhood and familial relationships.

But in the process of painting his own portrait he has, without
setting out to do so, given us a vivid picture of the archetype of
his generation. The Mexico of his youth is the one so familiar to

us who were his contemporaries. His home, strictly ruled by "Jarano," is typical of the pre-Revolutionary middle class: the ritual noonday meal with rice *a la mexicana*; the dignified poverty hidden beneath cleanliness and neatness; the terribly strict school discipline—and a child's dismay when he begins to notice discrepancies, prejudice, and injustice in the world he is about to enter.

In his "Word of Explanation" Ramón Beteta is careful to point out that his only purpose is to entertain the reader and give him a glimpse of a Mexico that no longer exists.

But he has done much more than that. He has shaped a dramatic human document in this account of the torments suffered by a superior mind in search of definition in the face of the most forbidding obstacles: poverty at home, lack of understanding at school, and the winds of revolution unleashed in all their fury. The link between his childhood years and those of the carefree, vigorous young manhood that were to lead him to the highest pinnacles of success is missing in this book. If he had lived another fifteen years, Ramón Beteta might have forged that missing link and gone on, openly and deliberately, to complete his memoirs.

The recollections he has left us in this little book, however, will serve as a foundation stone for the monument to the powerful personality of an illustrious Mexican—a monument raised not by words but by his contribution to his country. These few episodes, when read each one by itself, are like so many magnificent stories, imbued with the most pitiless and dramatic realism. As we read them we are astounded by his fine Proustian capacity for minute observation and bold evocation of atmosphere and situation. Let us watch this "nice boy" taking a Sunday walk with his father, hand in hand with the older brother whose love tenderly permeates every page of this book. Let us accompany the author as he roams through the old San Rafael district, or trudges along the dark streets toward Azcapotzalco, or has his first fight at the Tepanecos school, or suffers the traumatic frustration of winning a school prize he never receives, or is forced to dance "La Cucaracha" at rifle point. Let us join him as he sets out for Veracruz and describes the trip like a skilled novelist, or paints with the vivid palette of an Orozco the dreary and bitter scene when a stoical little Indian woman is raped by a group of ruttish soldiers.

Every facet of the life of an ordinary child tossed between two of Mexico's historic periods is thoroughly examined in these pages. We see his friendship with "the Bull," young Beteta's admiration for him, and their mutual exchange of interests. We are present at domestic scenes: in the author's home, in the opulent residences of his relatives, and in the household where the Bull enjoys the companionship of the understanding mother Ramón Beteta recalls with such affection.

Throughout this colorful gallery of personalities, types, and situations we feel the constant, implicit presence of his father: a father whose civic virtues, inculcated with severity but also with love and sympathy, were to be inherited by both of his sons. Here is Jarano, who evinces his pride in his country by forcing his children to don traditional costumes; the uncompromising Jacobin who aspires to see himself fulfilled in the son whose intelligence he has the wit to recognize and direct; the parent who sees the boy off at the railway station, overwhelms him with instructions, and gives him his last ten pesos.

Ramón Beteta intended Jarano to be the hero of this brief fabric of childhood memories and adult reflections, and chose his name for the title of the book he left unfinished and unrevised. He pictures Jarano's sumptuous, heavily-attended funeral—now that his sons have become men of importance in the world—when government officials, cabinet ministers, and even the President of the Republic gather to join the mourners (although the pitiless narrator, even in his grief, does not fail to surmise the worldly and "politic" motives in their condolences).

How many shining links, how many episodes in that resolute, vigorous career, would be needed to complete the chain of the autobiography he might have written! There would be his student years, here and abroad; his friendship with Moisés Sáenz, who was to become a stimulating colleague; his university associations with the generation that years later was to bring glory to Mexico; and the perfect accord of the binomial Ignacio-Ramón, symbolizing two aspects of the Revolution in which both served— that of arms in the case of the young man who in this book proudly displays his second lieutenant's bar, and that of letters in the case of the boy who induces the Bull to read *Don Quixote*.

It is in the last chapter—as the long procession winds toward the grave of the man who is "Jarano" to his sons and whom the mourners know only as the father of two distinguished men—that the author, struck by the cruel contrast between this and an earlier funeral, thinks back to someone he has merely sketched pages before and who plays no part in the book. His mother is merely mentioned and then suddenly disappears, as though she had no influence in the boy's life. But now we see that he has never forgotten her. Her frail, unsubstantial figure takes form as he recalls her death—a loss the child could neither believe nor accept. The memory is doubly painful when the tragic penury that surrounded her passing is compared with the pomp of the funeral that has brought it to mind.

And thus this book about Jarano, designed to end with his death, goes beyond that delimitation: the son's last thoughts, from a distance of many years, are of his mother. Here is the final confession of a man who regards the past with serenity and lucidity: "The red glow of sunset was rapidly disappearing from the sky. I felt that the afternoon had died, and that with it, and with my mother, my childhood had died also."

It was at that moment—to conclude this introduction to a distinguished Mexican's posthumous book—that Ramón Beteta was born for his country.

Salvador Novo

January 19, 1966

CONTENTS

JARANO

JARANO

A Word of Explanation

These are memories, but not memoirs. Memoirs, as a rule, are written as an apology for a way of life or as an interpretation of some public conduct—normally the author's. That is not the intent of these pages.

There are times, too, when memoirs serve to avenge oneself on some enemy against whom one was powerless at the time; since these are usually composed toward the end of one's life, when that enemy is dead, there is a certain odor of the autopsy about them. Neither is that the purpose of this book.

Like all memories, those that appear here are attenuated by

time and tinted by imagination. Thus they do not pretend to photographic accuracy or to rigorous historical value. What has occurred here is what often happens when we report some memorable conversation: knowingly or not, we round it out and embellish it with what we wish we had said at the time or with what we were hoping someone would say.

Though written in the first person because it is simpler and easier for the author to do so, not all of these recollections are of events within his own experience. Some were told to him by other people, who in turn had probably added their own touches to make them more interesting.

This is more a novel than a true story. The names the reader will find here are fictitious, except for those of public figures who are mentioned solely to fix dates or circumstances.

In short, the aim of this book is to entertain the reader and to give him a glimpse of a Mexico that no longer exists: the Mexico of the first half of this century, as seen through the eyes of a child and a young man. I hope it achieves that purpose.

A Nice Boy

No one who knows me today would believe it, and yet it's true:
I was a "nice boy." My parents dressed me in a sailor suit: the
blue pants and blouse, the white shirt with the open collar, the
wide silk necktie (also blue) tied in a bow, the patent leather
shoes and very thin black stockings, and the sailor cap with its
dangling white ribbon. No detail was missing. I even carried a
black wooden whistle tied by a stout cord to the pocket of my
blouse.

Anyone who knows my reputation for exhibiting and even culti-

vating bad manners has a perfect right not to believe me. But I can prove what I say: I was a nice boy. I still have photographs that leave no room for doubt. There is one in particular in which I am sporting all these trappings and, in addition, am holding an enormous, slender wooden hoop, with which I amused myself as became a child of my social class. If the "poor kids" wanted to roll a hoop along the gutter, they had to make do with a metal one from an old wine barrel and push it with any old twig. I used a swagger stick, like those the soldiers carried; it was smoothed and polished so I wouldn't get slivers in my hands.

Jarano

We called our father by his first name—Carlos—which, far from offending him or striking him as lacking in respect, gratified him; he was confident that such intimacy in no way lessened our filial love. For him, such a mode of address was an objective proof of his "broad-minded attitude"—as he called it—toward his children. Privately, however, my brother and I called him "Jarano." This nickname was used only by the two of us, unknown to anyone else, and there was an air of secrecy about it, and a special meaning. It expressed our father's aggressive Mexicanness; his liberality, excessive at times; our affection for him, not untinged

by respect and even by fear; and, at the same time, his inability
to understand certain things and his inconsistency, which often
bordered on caprice.

In our hearts we knew very well that it was not proper for us to
use such a nickname; but the word "Jarano" summed up so perfectly all that was, in our eyes, good and bad and above all
peculiar about our father, that having once adopted it we were
never able to give it up. We called him that until the day of his
death.

The incident that gave rise to the name was so typical of his
turn of mind that I cannot resist the temptation of relating it here.

Jarano was fascinated by horses and anything that had to do
with the Mexican cowboy, which was odd in view of the fact that
he was a city man who loved the capital and all it offered in the
way of amusements, night life, and conveniences. He had never
lived in the country nor owned a scrap of land, and it had never
crossed his mind to raise anything, even a plant in his garden at
home. But, as I say, he loved horses and instilled in his sons an
enthusiasm for every aspect of the equestrian art. We rode almost
as soon as we could walk.

One of my earliest childhood memories, in fact, is being astride
a little, old, grizzled horse that must have been slow and gentle
but seemed terribly tall and spirited to me. Jarano had probably
borrowed it from one of his friends. I was so small at the time
that a servant had to ride behind me to keep me from sliding off the
weary animal, for I often drooped over its neck and fell asleep.

Jarano rode whenever he could. This was not very often, for
he never could afford to keep even a miserable nag, let alone a
stable. And yet on the slightest provocation he would don his
charro costume, even when he was not going riding. He wore it to
bullfights, for example, or to village fiestas. This disturbed us

because it seemed incongruous. When we saw him in it we felt that peculiar kind of embarrassment we called "mu," which one experiences whenever someone makes a fool of himself. "Mu" is a feeling of misery *sui generis* characterized by the desire not to look at anyone—especially the subject—and is in direct proportion to the degree of kinship or intimacy that links us to the person who is making, or is about to make, a fool of himself. This happens, for example, when we are paying a formal call and our host's little daughter gets up to recite a poem with that intonation taught in grammar school; or when she sits down at the piano to display her musical gifts and makes a mistake on the first note; or when someone who has been persuaded to sing launches into a familiar operatic aria at the top of his voice and out of tune; or when a small-town politician forgets the speech he has prepared to welcome a candidate or the governor; or, finally, when the best man at a wedding, overcome by too many drinks, keeps mumbling the same thing over and over in congratulation of the bride and groom.

As long as my father's enthusiasm for the Mexican cowboy costume did not affect us directly, our suffering was limited to the "mu"; but there came a day when he decided that we, too, must wear charro suits. Worse yet, not the complete outfit, but only the sombrero and sarape—which Jarano called a *tilma*. It was not merely a matter of wearing them on trips to the country—which we wouldn't have minded at all—but of donning them for social calls, and even for school. This dress seemed absurd to us, and from the moment we were told of his decision we lived in torment at the thought of how our cousins and fellow students would laugh at us. We tried in every way to get out of it, but our protestations were useless. From the subsequent arguments and our rebellion sprang the nickname "Jarano."

This is how it came about. We were getting ready to pay a call at my maternal grandmother's house—the elegant Pavón y Pesqueira residence on Ribera de San Cosme Street, where we often spent the afternoon with the aristocratic old lady's numerous other grandchildren.

That day my father insisted that we wear the broad sombreros, like those used by real charros in the country, and the bright-colored *jorongos* or sarapes he had bought for us. The sombreros were rather cheap ones, without decoration. We had worn them for the first time on the previous Sunday on a trip to Tepexpan, where some of my father's clients—very modest country people—had invited us to spend the weekend. There, sombreros and sarapes had been perfectly suitable, as they protected us from the sun and the rain; and we had made the mistake of saying so. But to put them on now, for a visit to the San Rafael district on a clear afternoon, struck us as out of place and absurdly ridiculous. We were afraid, and with good reason, that everybody would make fun of us.

We tried to explain this to our father, but in vain. Weren't we already humiliated enough whenever our elegant cousins greeted us with, "Here come the kids from Number Two," referring to the "inside" number of our apartment? But Jarano insisted, with the adult's lack of understanding of a child's fine sensitivity to ridicule, which makes him miserable if his clothing is in any way different from that of his friends. Why should we care if they called us "the kids from Number Two"? That was, after all, our number on the "private street"—which was surely quite respectable—where we lived. And if we didn't have a whole house to ourselves, it was through no disinclination on his part, and we should be thankful we didn't live in a tenement in the heart of the city, as he had when he was a child. As for the sombrero, we had to admit that it was comfortable and in good taste, and protected us from the weather; and if our silly cousins made fun of it, it was because they liked to think of themselves as aristocrats, as though they were Limantours or Braniffs or Íñigos Noriegas. We, however, his children, were lucky enough to be real Mexicans and had no reason to admire Porfirio Díaz and his dictatorship; nor was there any occasion to think of ourselves as foreigners or to be ashamed of wearing the typical sombrero of our Motherland, the hat of the charro and the men of the soil: the *jarano*.

Jarano! It was the first time we heard the word. My brother and I exchanged a knowing look; the name had etched itself in our minds.

There was nothing to be done. We left the house in our sombreros and gaudy sarapes—mine was red and white, my brother's green and red—certain that everyone on the street would stare at us as a couple of queer specimens. If this had taken place fifty years later, people would have thought we were children of American tourists; but there were hardly any tourists in those days, from the United States or anywhere else.

The truth is that no one paid any attention at all to those two children walking in front of their mother along the nearly deserted streets of the San Rafael district. But we searched the faces of the passers-by, waiting for some humorous remark about our outfits. Nobody said a word, however, until we reached the gate of the family mansion where my grandmother lived. The gate opened onto the garden, a veritable park, across the street from the then famous Mascarones School. There that afternoon, as every Saturday, some of our thirty-six cousins and their friends were gathered. As soon as we came through the gate one of them called out: "Look at the kids from Number Two! They're all dressed up like charros!" Darío, the cousin we called "the General" because, in spite of being one of the youngest, he was always the leader in our games, deciding what we were going to play and who should take part, grinned at me and said, "What's doing, little cowboy? Did you come here on your dog?" This struck the others as terribly funny, and there was a roar of laughter. I didn't say anything, of course; but I was angry at being made fun of and yet at the same time quite willing to admit that my cousin's remark was justified.

We took off our sombreros and sarapes and began playing games, and my embarrassment passed. But all the rest of the afternoon I kept dreading the horrible moment when we would have to put them on again to go home.

Fortunately, it was dark by the time we left, and the sarapes were not as conspicuous. It was a cool evening, as most evenings in Mexico City are, and the blankets felt warm and comfortable. But the sombreros, those damned *jaranos,* seemed even more incongruous at night; in the daytime they at least sheltered us from the sun.

There were other experiences like this, each more unbearable than the last; but we never forgot that day when we first heard the word *jarano.* The *jaranos,* the *jarano* hats! My brother and I didn't even have to discuss it: the word was so typical of my father that it suited him perfectly as a nickname. Besides, we felt that we had invented a term with a special meaning of its own to be added to our vocabulary. From that day on "Jarano" was our father's name and *jaranadas* were the peculiar things he did; *enjaranarse* became a verb meaning to behave as he would have done; a *jaranismo* was any way of expressing oneself that was similar to his. His strange sense of humor, for example, would lead him to say in jest something disagreeable that the person addressed could easily take quite seriously; this was a *jaranismo.* He called these blunders his *pachotadas,* a word whose true meaning I never learned.* Also *jaranismos* were his peculiar ways of criticizing, correcting, or disagreeing with people by saying something that no one else would dare to put into words; the things he said often expressed very accurately an idea or situation that everyone admitted and accepted, but that was not mentioned in "polite society."

Although he did not mean to offend, these crudities were for Jarano the occasion of more than one unpleasantness; but he persisted in these blunt indiscretions, giving people his "frank opinion." To use another expression he was very fond of, he would not hesitate "to give the cock that crowed for Peter a piece of his mind."

So this new word took out naturalization papers in our family; even after we were grown up and married, we still spoke of committing a *jaranada* or being a *jarano*. Even our children, who had never known him and had no idea of the etymology of the term, used these expressions constantly.

Jarano heard of his nickname only shortly before he died. He found out about it, quite by chance, when he was already very ill; he merely smiled in an understanding way, without seeming to be offended, although it is most unlikely that he ever suspected the full meaning and flavor of the word. That secret name, for us, summed up his whole way of life.

* This is a common Spanish American mispronunciation of *patochada,* which very nearly corresponds to our "putting one's foot in it." *Tr.*

Sunday

Jarano must have loved us very much, even with his caprices and blind spots, and he tried to show it in his own way. One of his favorite manifestations was taking us for long walks on Sunday mornings; these generally ended on the Alameda Central, where we sat on a bench and listened to the military band. My brother and I went along hand in hand, pausing at the intersections like the well-brought-up children we were, under our father's vigilant and slightly anxious surveillance. I can still see his alert, myopic little eyes, glistening behind their spectacles: the brown, intelligent, expressive, shrewd eyes of the Mexican mestizo.

Sometimes our walks concluded with a visit to the bar of the

Saint Francis, an American hotel that was very fashionable at the time; it was a building in the European style on Juárez Avenue, quite near the corner where the statue known as "The Little Horse" stands today. There Jarano would order soft drinks for us and a brandy for himself. Our drinks were pink—we never learned what their ingredients were—and tasted like medicine to me. The flavor was rather like that of the cola drinks of today, which then were unknown. But we enjoyed them because we were in the company of grownups, in a place we thought very elegant.

Often the visit was too long. We grew bored with watching Jarano drink and hearing him talk about things we didn't understand. When we had finished our funny-tasting drinks, slowly consumed through a straw, we busied ourselves with searching the sawdust-strewn floor of the bar for cigar bands to add to our collections. Then we extended our expeditions to the lobby of the hotel and finally ended up at the front door, from where we watched the carriages and passers-by on Corpus Christi Street, now Juárez Avenue. After a while, tired and hungry, we returned to our father to wait impatiently for him to end his visit and take us home. We worried about staying too late, for we knew it would mean an argument; our getting home well past dinner time upset my mother as much as knowing by my father's breath that he had had more than one brandy.

Sunday dinner almost always ended in a small family tragedy. When Jarano drank he lost all appetite and wanted only to keep on drinking. In those days he refused to admit this openly, and tried to find some way to justify his lack of appetite to himself and, above all, to his wife. The system he adopted could not have been more unjust. It consisted of finding some alleged defect in every course. He used the same expressions again and again, to such a point that an impartial witness would have burst out laughing.

When the soup arrived he would pretend to taste it, and then ask, in a tone that was half jovial, half stern: "Will you please tell me what this dishwater is for?" When the soup has been taken away, amid affectionate *pro forma* protestations on the part of my mother, the rice was served. Jarano would examine it with an expert eye; he would spread it slowly and deliberately out over his plate; then he would make a wry face and announce regretfully that it was "all stuck together." In Mexican rice, he would observe in a professorial tone, each grain should be whole and separate. Then, with the air of someone who is making a great sacrifice, he would drown the whole plate of rice in a terribly hot green sauce, made especially for him from almost pure chile, and take a few mouthfuls—provided that the tortillas were not only hot but fresh from the griddle. After the rice came the meat course, which he invariably found inedible. Sometimes it was tough; other times it was too well-done; sometimes it was "nothing but skin"; occasionally he would simply push his plate away with the expression of a man who found it incredible that anyone should consider it fit for human consumption.

As dinner went on, the atmosphere in the dining room became more uncomfortable. In the face of these reiterated and unwarranted complaints, my mother in turn lost her appetite and a look of sickness and anger came over her face. My brother and I would gaze at each other in silence, knowing that the moment of the inevitable quarrel was approaching. I felt my heart beating faster, and had that unpleasant hollow feeling in the stomach that comes with fear. My hands began to sweat, my mouth was dry, and my throat tightened with a repressed impulse to burst into tears, until I could hardly swallow.

The storm would break over almost anything. Jarano, who had begun drinking again, generally turned to bestowing exaggerated

caresses upon one or the other of his sons. Often I was chosen. These shows of affection usually consisted of gently pinching my cheek or lovingly pulling my ear; and when the expression on my face fell short of his expectations he was astounded. In my state of mind at the moment, these attentions actively irritated me, and my attempts to hide my annoyance were futile. Then came the recriminations for what he called my "coldness" and my "insolence." Inexplicably, he would extend these accusations to my brother, who had done nothing at all. When he was in a bad mood, Jarano behaved as though he had a hidden dislike for him.

My mother would come to our defense, and that was when the dreaded scene began. Their voices rose, and strictures were mingled with lamentations: "Isn't it incredible that a man who is always punctual in handing over the household allowance can't get a single mouthful of food that isn't slop?" "What a terrible fate it is to have two sons who think they're the masters of the house!" If that was the case (he went on), we should go all the way and earn our living out in the world, as he had done in Oaxaca, instead of going around with that terrible martyred look on our faces and criticizing his behavior! Didn't we know that children have no right to judge their parents? When had ducks begun shooting at shotguns?

By that time we could no longer hold back our tears; we ran weeping to our mother, panic-stricken at the veiled threat of being driven out to earn our own living at the ripe ages of seven and ten, respectively.

The episode that followed was always the same. We were ordered out of the dining room and ran to hide in the little garden in front of the house, where we sobbingly discussed our tragedy, pausing now and then to listen when one of our parents tried to outshout the other. At last they quieted down, and my brother and I, still shaken, tried to comfort each other.

These horrible scenes, which would have seemed more stupid than calamitous to an adult, assumed in our eyes the proportions of a Greek tragedy, and were to have a definite influence on our lives. Whenever some misfortune befell either of us in later life, we always responded with the same mutual aid and comfort.

After the climax of these pointless disputes, my father would retire to his bedroom to take his usual Sunday siesta. When he awoke, at nightfall, he would let everyone know that he was still angry by leaving the house without saying good-by. We lay in bed, unable to sleep, until he came home. We knew his step so well that we could tell as soon as we heard him coming whether or not he was in the mood to carry on with the argument that had begun at dinner. Generally he was. The voices were hushed at first, then more audible, and finally loud and furious. We listened to them from our bedroom—this husband and wife entangled once again in their interminable, futile, and bitter dialogue.

As I wept silently on my pillow, not for the unpleasantness that was taking place in the adjoining room, but in self-pity, I would daydream of meeting with some accident—being run over by a streetcar, for example—that would bring great sorrow to my parents. Then they would realize how much I meant to them, and how badly they had treated me. In my excited imagination I could see it all quite clearly: I was running down Ribera de San Cosme Street, then carelessly crossing the wide avenue without seeing the tandem streetcar that hurtled toward me, then tripping and falling face downward on the tracks. I looked up and saw the huge yellow form bearing down on me; I could make out the letters that announced its destination, and, though I still could not read very well, I knew that they said "Tacuba." Then I felt a terrible pain. I tried to decide how serious the accident would have to be. Would I lose a leg? No. It would be better if I were killed. A crowd was gathering around the streetcar, which had stopped after hitting me. I saw from outside myself my motionless body, which some charitable soul had covered with a sarape; from beneath it oozed a great deal of red blood. And then I saw my father's distressed face approaching through the crowd. When he lifted the blanket and saw who it was, his grief was indescribable.

I would be so moved by this vision of my own death that I would begin crying again. As the hot tears ran down my face and soaked into the pillow, I felt sorry for my bereaved parents. While trying to decide which of the two—Jarano or my mother— would suffer more because of my catastrophe, I would fall asleep.

The Florencio

There were great arguments at home as to which school we should attend. All my cousins went to Mascarones, which had many advantages: it was right across the street from my grandmother's house, and we could get there without anyone's having to take us; it was a school for children of well-to-do families; and, above all, it was Catholic and run by Jesuits, no less.

My brother and I wanted to go there very much, not only because we saw our friends and relations coming out every afternoon, but because they played baseball, had a swimming pool, and gave big parties at the end of the school year. The government schools offered none of these things at the time.

There was not the slightest doubt in my mother's mind that it was the ideal school for us: her sisters recommended it, so it must be the best. But my father was absolutely against it. He was a liberal, and wanted his sons educated in a secular school; the Catholic institutions were operating in violation of the laws of the Reform; it was just one more example of the scandalous behavior of a dictatorship that had made a separate peace with the Church (on what grounds I never knew, my father attributed this shameful transaction to Doña Carmelita, Don Porfirio's wife); no, his sons would not be brought up as "right wingers"; they were not going to be taught to hate Don Benito Juárez, nor to blacken the spotless names of the men of the Reform—the best Mexico had produced in its entire history. Unhappily for our country, the Church's political influence was growing every day; the convents were no longer secret, everyone knew where they were. Nuns walked through the streets in their habits, unmolested; public services were being held more and more in the states of the central region, and even in the Capital itself—all in defiance of our laws. Such a state of affairs could not go on long. Soon there was going to be a civil war, for although the majority of Mexicans were Catholics they had no wish to be ruled by a foreign power such as the Vatican; they would revolt. The Revolution was at our gates; you could already feel it in the air, just as you could feel rain coming before the first drops fell. He wanted his children to be in no doubt as to which side they would choose in the coming struggle. True, he had been married in the Church and allowed his sons to be baptized; after all, he was no priest-hater, and religion was all very well in its place. But Church and State must be completely separated, as the Constitution of 1857 had decreed.

When my father got on this subject there was no stopping him. His in-laws finally gave up arguing with him, for they found it only made him worse. When he was opposed he grew more and more excited; he was carried away by the sound of his own voice, and no longer interested in the reactions of his captive audience. On these occasions my aunts would exchange silent glances; later they would tell each other, "Carlos has such funny ideas . . ." and touch the rosaries that usually hung at their waists.

But in the matter of our school Jarano was not merely obeying an oratorical urge. He sincerely believed in these ideas, and would not back down. A government school must be found for us. My mother had no choice but to submit; but she could not find one to her liking. She inspected several, but always came home with the same story: "It was a school for little paupers, for the children of housemaids." How could her sons go there! God only knew what diseases they might pick up, and what "little animals" they might bring home! But my father was adamant, and something had to be decided soon; my brother was no longer attending the Señoritas Ramos' kindergarten, where they taught Father Ripalda's catechism and cared for children of pre-school age, and at the moment was not receiving any instruction at all.

At last one afternoon my mother came home visibly pleased after one of these scouting trips. She had heard that a new school was opening in our neighborhood, the San Rafael district. She had visited the place, which was on Industria Street, quite near our house on Gabino Barreda. It was a brand-new *ad hoc* building—not like most she had seen, which were old residences made over. This school was different: it had modern bathrooms and a playfield, the classrooms were airy and sunny, and it was properly equipped with new furniture. But what appealed to her most was that (as she had been told "confidentially") it was to be only for children "of good families." It was understood—tacitly, of course —that little "street urchins" would not be admitted. The staff had been selected with the greatest care from the best Normal School graduates.

And so it was decided that we would attend the Florencio del Castillo School, which we always called "the Florencio."

My brother was enrolled at once. I had to wait for two years, during which time I watched my brother leave the house every morning with books and tablets under his arm or in a school bag on his back, and was terribly envious. When would I be old enough to go to school?

At last the longed-for moment arrived. I don't recall when or how I was enrolled, but I shall never forget my first day there. It must have been winter, sometime near the first of the year, for it was an unusually cold morning. As we stood in a row to be inspected for clean hands and faces before school began, we amused ourselves by watching our breath hang in the air in little clouds and pretending we were smoking. To my great surprise, many of my schoolmates wore gloves. I had never had a pair, and thought it was a sign of distinction and enormous wealth. My mother had not been deceived: the Florencio was a school for "nice children."

I still remember some of my fellow students. One was Magaña, who was very small and had slanted eyes like an oriental, though his skin was white; he dressed very properly, and was called for in a carriage that looked like a wicker basket, drawn by a pair of sorrels. In winter he wore woolen leggings that came up to his knees. I greatly admired these; but I was not envious, because it occurred to me that I wouldn't be able to play marbles in them without getting them dirty, and then my parents would scold me.

There was a friend of my brother's, a colonel's son; occasionally he invited us to play at his house. His family were well-to-do people in the Porfirio Díaz government.

Not all of us were rich, of course; but it was clear that considerable pains had been taken to make sure that none of us was really poor.

In my confused memories of my first year, only one experience stands out; it was one that I was ashamed of for a long time. My teacher, a young woman whom I thought very beautiful, was especially fond of me. One day, when morning classes were over, she kept me in the classroom to show me some little balls painted in many different colors—an abacus. Then she lifted me to her lap and tried to engage me in conversation. She knew that I had to wait for my brother to come for me, and I suppose she wanted to entertain me for a few minutes. I think she asked me if I liked school, but I wasn't paying attention; my mind was elsewhere. I was suffering from a horrible need to urinate, which I had barely been able to suppress until school was out. Every minute was an eternity. How could I beg that young lady, who was so loving and above all so pretty, to let me down for such a disgusting reason? An invincible embarrassment sealed my lips. At last I could no longer control myself. When she realized what had happened she stood up suddenly, staring in surprise at her wet skirt. I was paralyzed with terror, although I don't know exactly what I

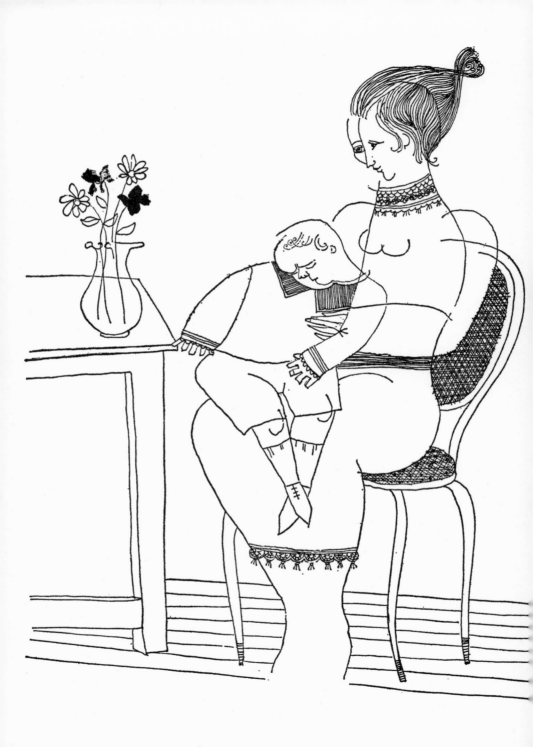

expected her to do to me. With a little smile she took me by the hand and led me to the bathroom—which by that time was useless. I was too nervous.

For a long time I recalled that episode with immense mortification. I never told anyone about it, not even my brother. It was the first great secret of my life.

Confused Years

My first three years of school left me with nothing more than a vague feeling of anxiety, which I would be hard put to account for. Perhaps it was due to my not having learned to read, while the other children seemed to have accomplished this. All I could make out in our primer, "A Family of Heroes," were a few short passages I had learned by heart but did not always understand. For some inexplicable reason, even the title confused me. I read it as "A Family of Herods," and vaguely recalled having heard of Herod in our Religion class.

I had a similar experience with some poems we had to memorize. There was one we recited in chorus, which was a hymn to the material progress achieved by Mexico under the regime of Don Porfirio. The poet had set out to describe the advances made by science in general and by our own country in that era of "peace and order." In his enumeration of new inventions he wrote, among other things, if my memory serves, the following:

> *...the glass that to the eye*
> *restores the vanished vigor,*
> *the wires that bear the voice*
> *that moves in mysterious fluid*
> *over colossal distances...*

But I combined the four last words of the first line into one, so that I thought "thatotheye" was some special thing made of glass. I don't know how long it was before I discovered my mistake and understood that the reference was to spectacles.

It wasn't until my fourth year that the Florencio made its greatest impression upon me. Up until then I had had young lady teachers, who had paid no special attention to me but had always been kind. My first male teacher was a Señor Pérez. He was a tall man—at least he seemed so to me—with a black mustache, and he was always very neatly dressed. My first impression was a favorable one, perhaps because he had a pleasant smile that displayed very large, white, even teeth. But this impression soon vanished. During roll call the first day my name struck him funny: "Beteta . . . Are you sure it isn't *Mirateta?*"*
The whole class laughed at his joke, which now that I write about

---

* This play on words is possible because initial *b* and *v* have the same sound in Spanish. Thus "Beteta" is pronounced the same as the phrase *ve teta* (he sees the tit). By substituting an analogous verb, the teacher has produced *mira teta* (he looks at the tit). *Tr.*

it seems innocent enough—although perhaps not the most suitable for children of our age. But at the time it struck me like a slap in the face, like an unwarranted insult; it seemed a discourtesy toward my ancestors, an accusation of some shameful act. The blood rose to my face and my ears burned; all my initial liking for him had disappeared.

That lack of sympathy was soon to be replaced by genuine aversion. Señor Pérez' whole pedagogical theory was founded on a single principle, which squared perfectly with the political and social atmosphere of the time: school children must remain motionless and silent. There must be order and no noise—these were the indispensable requisites for education. Indeed, they were the end of education itself. As soon as we arrived in the morning we had to line up in a row; after cleanliness inspection we marched —one, two, one, two—into the classroom. In taking our places we followed another strict ritual that divided the movement into three parts. At the count of one we raised our seats; on two, we took one step to the right and stood behind our desks; on three, we all sat down with a great clatter. Nothing pleased the teacher more than hearing all the seats fall at the same instant, with a single clack. When we were in our places, Señor Pérez would call out, "First position!" Like little automatons we put our hands, palms down, on our desks. We held this position for an indeterminate period, until the next order: "Third position!" This one, which was inserted among the other three and was intended to be restful, consisted of clasping our hands behind our heads. It was usually held only briefly; then we would either go back to the first or be ordered to proceed to the second, in which we sat with folded arms. In the fourth position, which was used less than the others, we were obliged to put our hands on our shoulder blades, with our knuckles touching the back of the seat.

We were allowed to move only when changing from one position to another, and then only on command. For me, this immobility was sheer martyrdom. I liked to sit sideways, or rest my elbows on the desk, or slide down in my seat until only my head was visible. I enjoyed exchanging comments with my neighbors, and felt that it was perfectly legitimate to ask small favors of them: an eraser, a pencil, a knife. And, finally, I liked to pass the time drawing meaningless doodles on a scrap of paper, which did not really divert my attention from the class. But any of these activities was in violation of one or both of the school's fundamental principles: immobility and silence.

I do not argue the pedagogical merits of the system. And yet for a child as restless and nervous as I was, it demanded the impossible. As a result I was continually being scolded. Now because of my hands; now because I was not sitting correctly; now because I had turned my head; now because I was drawing "pothooks," as my fantastic designs were called. Scolding gave way to punishment. At first I was deprived of the half-hour morning recess, and confined to the classroom to work at some special task. Later I was kept after school, even after having been made to stand in the corner during class. Finally they improved the system to the point where I not only had to stay after school from five until six o'clock, but was obliged to remain standing the whole time.

I would watch the other children leave with a great sadness, not untinged with fury, for I was convinced that I was the victim of an injustice. All my plans for playing after school were ruined; my friends, naturally, would not wait for me, and by the time I was able to join them they had already organized their games without including me.

No one could validly claim that these punishments were disproportionate or excessively cruel; but their effect was cumulative. Far from inspiring remorse or any inclination to mend my ways, they drove me to lay new plans for revenge. In my child's mind I felt that if I continued doing things that annoyed the teacher and showed him that I was indifferent to the penalties he imposed, it would be a way of getting even. This, inevitably, resulted in further punishment, which in turn produced in me the same reaction. Thus I entered upon a vicious circle.

When half an hour's detention had grown to an hour and a half, and then finally two, the teacher was faced with a new problem: who was going to remain in charge of me? For if Señor Pérez stayed with me, he would be penalized as well as I. He hit upon the idea of leaving me with the janitor; but as the man often had to go into his apartment for something, or was busy cleaning the other classrooms, I was able to escape easily. After this had happened several times the janitor took to locking me in one of the rooms on the ground floor. The first time, in despair, I stayed there the whole two hours. The next time, however, I tried to force the door; and when that didn't work I turned my attention to the windows. They were of the sliding sash type we call "guillotines," and could not be locked with a key. I was soon able to get one open and jump out, without hurting myself much. I landed on the soft ground in the middle of one of the garden plots where, to inspire us with a love of agriculture, our class had been made to plant vegetables. The damage I did to these crops, naturally, aggravated my offense.

The next day, before I had a chance to explain what had happened, I was told that I was to be kept in again. This time they took me up to the second floor. Thus began a kind of competition between the school authorities' determination to confine me and my cleverness at escaping. In this game I kept finding new ways to get out of the room where they had locked me. Once I broke a window into the hall, went down the stairs, and left by the front door without anyone seeing me.

By that time I felt like a hardened criminal, which was what my teacher kept calling me. Soon there were other developments that made my situation even worse. My erstwhile attention in class, which had been total although my "positions" left a great deal to be desired, began to fall off—especially when I had to listen from a standing position. Now, determined to show my schoolmates that these punishments didn't bother me a bit, I began trying to make them laugh by clowning and making faces from my dunce's corner. As my proficiency increased, so did my punishments. The teacher, in despair, at last expelled me from the room. I wandered forlornly about the school yard, feeling apprehensive and very wicked; but no thought of reformation ever once crossed my mind.

Under these circumstances I became not only perverse and unruly, but lazy—and, as a consequence, stupid. This last was something I at first refused to admit. I was bad, yes. This rancor of mine, this desire for revenge, were undoubtedly, as the teacher said, due to some innate evil in me. And I was disobedient, too— no one could deny that! Although how could anyone be expected to obey a teacher who demanded such impossible, absurd things? But it had never occurred to me that I was stupid. My father had told me a thousand times, publicly and privately, that I was a quick, intelligent, and talented boy. I understood adults' conversations and could make very sensible observations on them, he said. My remarks were opportune and even clever and witty, he found. No one had ever called me stupid. Nevertheless, I was gradually coming to believe that the teacher was right. He would call on me at a moment when my attention was wandering—

these moments occurred more frequently every day—and either I didn't even hear his question or only half heard it, and, naturally, didn't understand what he was asking. Then he would hold me up before the class as an example of an imbecile who couldn't even understand Spanish. What could anyone ever expect from me? He would announce that he pitied my parents for having such a son, and our Motherland for having to put up with such useless future citizens. I belonged to the scum of society; I would grow up to be a parasite, a criminal, a public enemy; I would be incapable of earning a living, for with my poor physique I could not hope to be even a laborer. These denunciations always concluded in the same way: I was a hopeless case, and would end my days in prison or on the gallows.

Convinced that all of this was true, and disappointed in myself, I began to withdraw into an imaginary world of daydreams, in which I was invariably the victim. I enjoyed this self-inflicted suffering, and spent many hours absorbed in my fantasies. I grew to prefer them to ordinary children's games. My homework became more difficult for me every day, and ended by being hateful to me. I had no inducement to do anything, and too little will power to overcome either my absent-mindedness or my sloth. And so the teacher's predictions came true: I was wicked, lazy, and stupid, and obviously would grow up to be an unproductive and dangerous human being.

In desperation at the problem I presented, Señor Pérez changed his tactics and became sarcastic. When he had asked a hard question that no one was able to answer, he would turn to me and say with feigned sweetness, "Let us hear what our star pupil, the industrious Ve Teta, has to say." Then he would repeat his question, which, of course, I couldn't answer. Señor Pérez would

shake his head pityingly and exclaim, "Imagine that! He doesn't
know! How odd!"

He was probably trying to stimulate me; but these slaps in the
face, far from achieving their object, only depressed me more. I
was willing to concede that I was lazy and perverse and stupid.
I had come to believe that there was nothing I could do about it:
it was my nature to be this way. Then why did he keep harrassing
me? It must be because the teacher had a diabolical urge to see
me suffer.

As the end of the year approached my parents were advised
that because of my poor conduct and lack of achievement I would
not be passed. My father, to whom his sons' education was a
matter of prime importance, was terribly upset. After his first
angry outburst, a long speech giving vent more to disappointment than to wrath, he calmed down and began talking to me in
an affectionate way, trying to understand the problem. He had
faith in me; he knew perfectly well that I was a smart boy with
good judgment; he could not believe what he had been told. What
had happened at school? At these words the dam broke. The
tears that had been held back for so many months streamed from
my eyes in a torrent. I wept for a long time, and my sobs must
have been heard all over the house. At last, gasping, I was able to
explain that the teacher hated me. He had taken a dislike to me
from the first moment. He had made fun of our name; he had
punished me unjustly; and I had turned into a bad boy. Jarano
listened with rare calm, and then said, "Look here—I don't believe in siding with a child against his teacher. I tell you *a priori*
that he's right in the matter; but I must confess that I don't understand what has happened. Tomorrow I'll go see the principal and
find out what's been going on. As for you, promise me you'll

behave yourself and not humiliate me by flunking." I gave my tearful promise and, for the first time, resolved to turn over a new leaf.

I went to school the next morning filled with great hopes. That day, for a wonder, there were no punishments pending. Now I was really going to be a good student. I had even planned to go to the teacher and tell him of my determination to reform; but unfortunately there was no opportunity. As soon as I arrived we lined up like soldiers in the schoolyard. Then we listened to the principal, who was in the habit of giving us bits of advice or simple harangues or making some announcement every morning before school. After that we marched into our rooms while the teachers called out, "One, two, one, two . . ." We stood beside our desks. "One, two, three," and we took our seats. "Second position!" and we folded our arms. Now there was no chance to speak to the teacher, or even to move—much less to make a public announcement of my decision.

Lessons began. I made heroic efforts to pay attention, but after so many months of letting my mind wander it was not easy. I sat up straight and tense in second position, my eyes fixed on the teacher, determined not to miss a word. Suddenly Señor Pérez broke off and said to me in a stern voice, "What's the matter, boy? What do you mean by staring at me like that?" Taken by surprise, I could only answer, "Nothing, Sir, nothing at all." He went on with the lesson, but the spell had been broken. It was becoming harder and harder to concentrate. I kept my eyes on the teacher, but his figure seemed to be growing smaller, as though he were moving away and becoming less real. The prescribed immobility was more unbearable every moment. But I was determined to keep my promise to my father, and continued sitting there without moving a muscle, although I was understanding less and less. All at once, to my surprise, my interest was awakened. It was the word "skeleton" that made me prick up my ears. He was not speaking of dead people, however. He was referring to the metal framework of what was going to be the House of Congress—a building every Mexican should be proud of, he said. At this point it was just a steel skeleton, but eventually Congress would meet under its roof. Did we know what Congress was? No? Well, it was made up of two Houses: the Senators and the Representatives. These were very distinguished men whom the people chose periodically to represent them and to defend their interests. They were an integral part of the government, which was made up of three Powers: the Legislative, the Executive, and the Judicial. The Executive was the President of the Republic. Mexico was now blessed with a magnificent President: Señor General Don Porfirio Díaz, a hero of peace as well as of war. It was to him that our country owed its order, its freedom, its full employment, its prosperity, and, above all, its peace. After his heroic struggle against the foreign invader, Don Porfirio had brought peace and prosperity to Mexico. We must keep this fixed in our minds, because we were going to learn a new verse of the National Anthem, which dealt with the very things he had been explaining. He would write it on the blackboard, and we were to copy and memorize it. We would have to sing it at the next school General Assembly, on the following Saturday.

The teacher took a piece of chalk and began to write the new stanza on the board, and I set to copying it mechanically. But a confusion had sprung up in my mind, making it hard to write the words correctly. How was it that my father always referred to Don Porfirio as a dictator who had brought an end to political freedom in Mexico, oppressed the people, and established an inequitable economic regime under which the populace was starving? And then how could our teacher tell us that he was a veritable hero and a magnificent president? Who was lying to me? My natural inclination was to believe my father, but at the same time I had great respect for my teacher's opinions.

I was still deep in these ruminations when someone behind me broke the silence with an imitation of a cat: "Miaow." I turned my head to see who had been so daring. Just at that moment Señor Pérez, too, turned around.

"That was you, Beteta! It must have been you!" he barked. My blood froze.

"It wasn't me, Sir, honest it wasn't," I said, holding back the tears. "I just turned around to see who did it."

"We'll see. Show me what you've written."

The page in my notebook was almost blank.

"Being a liar is a new quality I didn't know you possessed. On your feet, and you will remain after class at noon. I want to talk to you."

The morning seemed interminable. Since I had given up paying attention to what was going on in class, the hours crept by very slowly; my imagination ran wild trying to guess what new punishment would occur to the teacher, and wondering how I was going to explain this to my father. At last the lesson ended and my schoolmates left. My mouth was dry and my heart was pounding; I searched my mind for some way to salvage my plan of regeneration.

To my great surprise he merely said, "Write a hundred times: 'I am not to interrupt in class.' In ink, with no mistakes. I'm going to the principal's office, and when I return we'll have a talk."

On the right side of my desk there was an inkwell that fit snugly in a hole in the top. It was simply a little glass cup with an opening just large enough to admit the steel pen at the end of a slender holder made of cheap wood. To remove the inkwell, you had to reach under the desk and push it upward, or you could pull it out of its hole by inserting your finger in the opening. If you used the latter method you always got ink on your fingers, and it was forbidden. I saw that mine had ink in it, and began filling the first page of my notebook by writing "I, I, I, I . . ." in a vertical row down the left-hand side of the page until I came to the bottom, and then beginning at the top again with "am, am, am, am . . ." I felt that in this way the writing would be neater than if I wrote the complete sentence, "I am not to interrupt in class," straight across on each line. I had just finished the first page of thirty sentences when Señor Pérez came back. He was walking fast. In his right hand he held the heavy black wooden ruler he used to point out things on the blackboard. He was furious. He planted himself in front of me and said, "So little Beteta has complained to his papa that we don't love him!"

"No, Sir . . ." I began.

"Silence!" he snapped. "Do you know what you need? A good beating—and I ought to give you one, since you don't get it at home."

He came toward me with the black ruler in his hand. I stood up between the seat and the desk, filled with a strange mixture of fear and rage.

"You can't hit me," I said, hardly able to get the words out. I dropped my pen and began rolling it nervously across the desk. My fingers came upon the little hole in the top of the inkwell.

"I can't, eh? Watch this."

I felt a blow on my left shoulder. As I recall, it didn't hurt much, and I doubt if it was a heavy one. It felt more like an electric shock. My father had always told me that teachers in the government schools were forbidden to strike the children. How could

this man do it? I was trapped between the back of my seat and the desk, threatened by a man immeasurably stronger than I, and he was beginning to beat me. This was no teacher, because teachers were not allowed to hit their students; he was just an ordinary man who was taking advantage of his size and strength.

Somehow I had managed to pull the inkwell from its socket, and stood holding it in my right hand.

"No! No! You can't hit me!" I cried, trembling with anger. Then I saw the inkwell fly through the air and strike the teacher just below the collar. He stood there, paralyzed. Not only had the ink splashed over his clothes, but it had spattered his face and was slowly running down his cheeks. The purple fluid stood out vividly against his terribly pale skin. One drop had landed near his eye, and was falling like some strange, dark tear. Señor Pérez bared his white teeth in a grimace that was intended to be a smile. I stood stock-still before him, horrified at what I had done and dreading the consequences, which I was sure would be a real beating. All my anger had melted away; I felt completely hollow inside as I waited for his reaction. I hardly cared what was going to happen to me, but I wished something would. The silence seemed interminable.

"Look, Beteta," he said at last. "You can thank God that I'm not allowed to give you what you deserve. But I can promise you one thing: you won't pass this year. Now get out."

I ran. I crossed Industria Street and raced up Guillermo Prieto, which they were beginning to pave with asphalt. I didn't stop running until I reached Gabino Barreda. There I came to a halt; I was nearly home, and wanted time to think. What would I tell my father? How was I going to explain it to my brother? Would they expel me from school? And then would they put me in some reform school? A steam roller was going back and forth over the hot asphalt that had been spread out on the street in particles a little larger than a marble. I liked the odd odor. As I stood watching the workers I reflected that one of those little black balls could be made into a real marble if you let it cool off and then polished it. I went to the curb and picked one up cautiously. It was not hot enough to burn my hand, but it stuck to my fingers and I was unable to shape it into a regular sphere. With blackened fingers which I tried unsuccessfully to rub clean on a house front, I went on my way, feeling calmer. At home I said nothing to anyone. I pretended to be sick, and went to bed without supper.

The next day I couldn't find the courage to tell my father, or even to discuss it with my brother. I went to school filled with apprehension, but found nothing changed—except that Señor Pérez now looked right through me, as though I were invisible. My first reaction was one of great relief, for I was no longer under such tension. But as the hours and days went by I began to be seriously concerned. The teacher never again addressed a word to me. He never again asked for my homework, nor gave any sign that he knew I was there. Then I began to realize that my fate was sealed: I would not pass. This knowledge saddened me deeply, mostly because of the promise I had given my father. As the finals approached I decided to speak to him about it. I tried several times, but couldn't work up the courage until the day before the exams. Then I simply announced to Jarano that the teacher had said he was going to fail me, without giving any details. My father offered to attend the examinations with me, and did so. Señor Pérez, seeing him there, called on me several times. Usually my answers were wrong, not only because of my ignorance but because the presence of my father and the whole situation had made me extremely nervous. As we left, my father said, "They're going to flunk you, and you deserve it. You've given me the greatest sorrow of my life."

That summer vacation was a gloomy one.

My father hired a tutor for me during the summer, so that I would be prepared to take a special examination and pass the year that I had failed. It had been arranged to put me in another school, where my tutor was one of the faculty; there I was to take my special examination and thus regain normal standing. Fortune, however, was not smiling on our family in those days; these plans were never carried out. My father lost his job in one of the civil courts, and we had to economize. Since the tutor's fees were one of the easiest expenses to eliminate, my private lessons ceased, and I had to resign myself to repeating my fourth year. Luckily, Señor Pérez had moved on with his group to the fifth; the new teacher, who knew nothing, or pretended to, of the incident that had occurred with his predecessor, treated me like anyone else. Thus, with no major obstacles to overcome, I succeeded in getting through the year.

And Misfortunes Rained ...

That year misfortunes rained on our house. After my father lost his job the family finances went downhill rapidly. Finding another position was not easy for anyone who had no "pull," and even harder for a man known to be a liberal and a Mason—thanks to my father's long anticlerical harangues. Under pressure from his wife and his sisters-in-law, who insisted that he must do something to counteract the intrigue that had cost him his job, he finally gave in and grudgingly agreed to ask Don Ramón Corral to use his influence. Don Ramón was an old schoolmate of my maternal grandfather—Doctor Benito Pavón y Pesqueira. It could not be truly said that he was a close friend of the family, although at home we spoke of him as though he were. The simple truth was that Corral had called on Doña Josefita—my grandmother—a few times after Don Benito's death, and that my parents had been invited occasionally to the magnificent receptions held at Don Ramón's elegant mansion on Artes Street—which they had never forgotten. Moreover, there was a political element uniting them: all our family and friends were decided Corralistas and rabid anti-Reyistas.* The women, especially, all my aunts and cousins, boasted of this affiliation, and made their husbands wear white carnations in their buttonholes to proclaim their Corralismo to the four winds. All this made them confident that he would gladly use his influence to find Jarano a position.

And yet, Corral's very eminence made the matter more difficult. By that time Don Ramón was too important and too involved in the serious problems of the presidential succession to concern himself with something as trivial as getting a job for a friend who was out of work. What happened is what usually happens in such cases. My father spent countless hours cooling his heels in long anterooms and then being told each time to come back tomorrow; at last the day came when the officious uniformed usher informed him that "His Excellency the Vice-President regretted that he would be unable to see him, and begged him to discuss the matter with his private secretary." When this gentleman was at last able to find time for him, he heard my father out with thinly disguised impatience, and made a note of the case to be forwarded to the Vice-President. "You will be advised by mail as to the disposition

* Ramón Corral and Bernardo Reyes were expected to be contending candidates in an election to replace Porfirio Díaz as President of the Republic, but this election never took place. *Tr.*

of your application," he said, concluding the interview. And so
ended the long, tedious, futile gesture.

With all hope of finding a government job gone, my father decided to open a law office. This move had a very good psycho-
logical effect on him. He had always dreamed of "being his own
boss." At last he had attained the goal of a lifetime: to earn his
living in the practice of the profession that had cost him so much
sacrifice and hard work. He even looked different: he seemed
younger, held himself more erect, and lost much of the bureau-
cratic air he had acquired during those long years of petty admin-
istrative and judicial posts in Oaxaca and Mexico City. He took
greater care with his personal appearance. Every morning, after
shaving with the greatest care with a straight razor stropped on a
kind of leather belt hung at the head of his bed, he would annoint
his mustache with a white, faintly perfumed pomade and bind it
in place with a curious transparent ribbon he called a "mustache
cover." This was tied firmly behind his head and kept on for quite
a while to make sure that the points would remain curved and
erect, like the tails of two angry scorpions. They always made me
think of bicycle handlebars. Then he meticulously knotted his
"cravat," and brushed his double-breasted frock coat and derby
with an expert hand. After having adjusted his attire before the
big mirror of the black wardrobe in his room, he left the house,
cane in hand, with a firm step and went to his office, feeling important, distinguished, and (we used the English word) "suc-
cessful."

He had set up his "chambers," as he invariably called them, on
Donceles Street. They were typical of his time and class. There
were two rooms: a waiting room and another marked PRIVATE.
The first held a set of black furniture with cane backs and seats: a
sofa, two armchairs (one was a rocker), and several straight

chairs. They had been bought secondhand, "cheap and in perfect condition," as he told his wife the day he acquired them. At the rear of the room stood a small pine table painted some dark, indefinite color, behind which Don Rodrigo, his secretary, assistant, and porter, sat in silence for hours on end. Don Rodrigo was a man worn out more by illness, toil, and poverty than by age; he had once held with great dignity the post of concierge in the Capital's City Hall. It was only because he received a small pension that he could live on the tiny salary my father could afford to pay him. As his handwriting was good and he was familiar with the courts, he was able to serve as secretary as well as messenger boy— although his principal function was announcing clients.

Bent and smiling, in his shabby but clean clothes, Don Rodrigo fitted into the office perfectly. At night my father would dictate long legal documents to him, which he would copy out in longhand during the day, his arms clad in black sleeve-protectors.

The walls of the waiting room were adorned with diplomas and credentials, in gaudy gilt frames, proclaiming the occupant of the office to be a bona fide graduate in Law from the Oaxaca Institute and a member of various scientific and honorary societies. In the middle of these, framed in the same way, hung a conspicuous notice that read: THERE WILL BE A FEE FOR ALL CONSULTATIONS.

A brass plate fastened to the door leading into the next room bore, in beautifully engraved letters, my father's name and professional degree. Inside the "private office" an old, bulky roll-top desk and several shelves filled with carefully aligned and well-worn volumes of jurisprudence and statutes lent the desired judicial air. When the top of the desk was up, there could be seen rather neat piles of papers, newspaper clippings—my father liked to save and reread editorials—and a metal letter opener. Behind them were many little drawers with knobs, whose contents, which aroused my childish curiosity, I never dared to investigate. A swivel chair in front of the desk seemed to cry out every time its owner sat down in it. This chair was a kind of symbol of his dignified calling; perhaps that was why my brother and I, on the few occasions when we visited his office, were never allowed to sit in it. The furnishings were completed by another sofa and several unmatched straight chairs for the accommodation of clients.

In spite of these preparations and the expectations they implied, the cases that passed through his office were few and insignificant, and I doubt if the handful of clients who entered it were particularly scrupulous in observing the pointed announcement on the waiting room wall. This was to be expected, for my father lacked the necessary connections to succeed as an attorney; and he was in no position to make any, for everyone in business was connected, in one way or another, with the government—which he called the "Higher-Ups"—and he was now denouncing the regime more openly than before at every opportunity. He was especially voluble in the midst of the group of friends whom he met every day at a bar near his office for a drink before lunch.

So it turned out that the office merely increased expenses without bringing in enough income to offset them.

An inheritance from my grandmother came along to improve the situation, but not for long. Doña Josefita had had the wit to hold onto, if not to increase, the legacy left by Don Benito, and was rightly believed to be a very rich woman. But when her fortune came to be divided up among seven daughters and thirty-six surviving grandchildren, it melted away "like salt in water," as my Aunt María used to say. María was fond of similes, and often lamented that her mother's money had slipped through our fingers "like a handful of sand."

This was actually the case. Thanks to my grandmother's will, none of the heirs was able to maintain the standard of living he had enjoyed up until that moment. It turned out that the inheritance dwindled away during the long years of troublesome litigation—not only because of court costs and taxes, but because the many relatives who had always depended upon my grandmother had to be supported. When, at last, the executors came to an agreement that was not very clear and that involved a rather complicated system of distribution, serious difficulties came up. The legacy consisted mostly of real estate, which was not easy to divide. Family relationships were further strained because of the fact that the principal beneficiaries were women. Some were already widowed, and all were totally ignorant when it came to business dealings, as only "well-brought-up ladies" of that era could be. This made them, under the influence of their children, suspicious of any proposed compromise as a manipulation on the part of their coinheritors to strip them of their rightful due.

This situation occasioned forced sales and hastily drawn mortgages to satisfy the demands of the more impatient members of the family—especially the young people who had been waiting only to receive their shares in order to get married. These transactions made considerable inroads into the amount that was to be divided up, and in the end nobody was satisfied. And so, along with the inheritance disappeared the cordiality and unity that had always prevailed in our family.

My mother's share of that legacy, which we all had hoped would be the solution to our financial problems, was a house and a small sum in cash. The house was the one in which my brother and I had lived all our lives. It had been built for my parents on the parklike grounds of my grandmother's "big house" soon after their wedding, as had been done for each of her sisters when they married. This was a tradition Doña Josefita scrupulously followed in order to maintain the unity of the family; as her daughters were married, houses were built for them, although they were not given the land on which they stood. "It's another home within the home, so the children can live apart and still be together," she used to explain to strangers who were surprised to see those independent dwellings within a closed area, in each of which was multiplying a branch of the "tribe." As my grandmother had jealously guarded her rights to the whole, granting the property to her daughters and their husbands only in usufruct, the family was in fact kept together. But with her death, and later with the opening of Altamirano, García Icazbalceta, and Industria streets (the last is now Serapio Rendón), which cut across the estate, the houses were separated; and the families were not long in withdrawing from one another and moving away. The estate was mortgaged to meet the costs of the litigation and then sold to satisfy the debt. The money my mother received was part of the proceeds from this sale.

As soon as my parents got their inheritance they proceeded to spend it. First they decided to buy new furniture for the "reception room," which we didn't really need; and once it had been delivered, we had to give a party to show it off. Every member of the family was outfitted with new clothes. My mother hardly ever went out in those days, and yet—against her protestations, which certainly sounded convincing enough—my father bought her an expensive evening gown. It was of green velvet, and cut quite low. I saw her in it only once, but I remember being struck by her pallid skin and blond hair, which gave her an unhealthy look that was not without a certain beauty. He also bought her a complete outfit for "street wear," including an enormous hat covered with trimmings. She wore it to my eldest cousin's lavish wedding.

In addition to his new suit and shoes, my brother was given the money for a bicycle, which he innocently bought secondhand from a little hole-in-the-wall agency. When he proceeded to apply for a license he realized that they had not given him a bill of sale; but when he went back for it the dealer absolutely denied having sold him anything. Thus the bicycle had no legal existence, and without a license was not of much use to anyone.

As for myself, I insisted on having a tricycle like the one I had seen in an American catalogue. I had to wait several months for it to come from San Antonio, Texas.

Once the legacy had been frittered away on such trifles, our only hope was my father's law practice. By that time, however, the Revolution had broken out, and the courts were functioning so irregularly that their doors were often closed for long periods. The small cases my father had been able to get could naturally no longer be processed, and eventually they ceased altogether. With this our situation became really critical. At home we lacked even the most basic necessities. My father often had to go out "to look for something to do" without being able to leave my mother any household money; she got by as best she could, but it was becoming harder and harder. At first she was able to get credit. She owed the storekeeper, the milk vendor, the Spaniard who ran the bakery on Guillermo Prieto Street, and even the Indian woman who brought tortillas every day. At last these people began demanding their money on delivery. Something had to be done. My parents made a heroic decision: we would sell the house, all that remained of our inheritance.

It was a severe blow for my mother. The home was to her a symbol of economic security and social position. Losing it meant losing her last foothold, sinking in her own estimation and in that of her friends and relatives. In order to make this up to her to some extent, her husband bought a house in the Coachilco district in the town of Azcapotzalco; but it was a much more modest one, and far from the center of the Capital. It was a radical change. Our new home had only one story and was built of adobe; it was at a considerable distance not only from Mexico City but from Azcapotzalco itself. Coachilco was more like a separate town than a district. Besides, the house could not boast even the most basic conveniences. The water, of questionable potability, had to be drawn from a shallow well with a hand pump. It had no drains or electric lights. The bathroom was conspicuous by its absence. I have never understood my father's reasons for buying such a piece of property in such a remote location. It was perhaps the only area in the Federal District where property values never rose, not even when peace returned to the country and the prices of city houses and lots multiplied in an extraordinary fashion. Thirty-five years later Coachilco was still the same gloomy, dirty, ugly place it was the day we moved into that house—which my brother and I ironically called "the castle."

More than the discomfort of her new home, my mother resented having to move away from the section of the city where she had grown up. She was now far from her sisters, and it was difficult for them to visit her. This depressed her—although this sadness may have been due in part to her illness, which was advancing rapidly.

Tepanecos

My new school was on Tepanecos Street in Azcapotzalco. The name of the street struck my brother funny; he used to tease me by calling me a "Tepaneco" and referring to the school as the "Tepaneco Institute."* This is the name I remember, and not the real one, which was the Vicente Alcaraz School.

I spent my fifth and sixth school years there. Although it was an especially difficult time for me because of our extreme poverty,

* Tepanecos (or Tepanecas, Tecpanecas) were the ancient Nahua Indians who founded Azcapotzalco. *Tr.*

I remember them with affection and nostalgia. This may be because the school made a profound impression on me, and taught me a great deal about what our country really is—something that "properly brought-up" children never learn.

I was the only child in Tepanecos who wore shoes. My fellow students wore huaraches or went barefoot. When we lined up in the yard in the morning before school, a penetrating odor of the stable filled the air. To me, who often arrived without having had any breakfast, or at the most some watery coffee I had made for myself in the rustic kitchen of our old house in Coachilco, the smell was far from offensive. It brought back memories of milk fresh from the cow; thick, sweet hot chocolate; hot biscuits; and the breakfast-table conversation of a family making plans for the day. None of these things existed for me now. And so, instead of feeling sorry for my little schoolmates with their dark skin, their white teeth, and their cheeks glowing with health and sun, who had gotten up at dawn to milk the cows before coming to school, I envied them their lot. They had all grown up on farms, and most of them were descendants of the aboriginal Indians. To them I was a rich boy. The vivid contrast between their white cotton trousers and shirts and my black wool suit, buttoned up to the collar, made them look upon me as a strange creature, a kind of intruder. They believed that I enjoyed luxuries they had never known, and took a dislike to me. How were they to know that under those patched and repatched trousers there was no underwear? How could they suspect that within those shoes, carefully polished with blacking and spit, my toes were protruding from my lisle stockings? (I had futilely tried to mend them as though I were sewing up a sack, and, naturally, they had ripped open at the first few steps.) And, above all, how could they understand—these children for whom poverty was a natural, accepted, and

honorable way of life—how ashamed I was of having no under-
clothes and holey stockings that I washed myself? How could they
comprehend that all these were, to my mind, evidence of my
disastrous present and my totally hopeless future?

One of my greatest humiliations came to me one afternoon at
the house of one of my relatives. I had shown up just at dinner
time, hoping for an invitation, and was feeling rather embarrassed about it—although everyone pretended not to know that
my call was prompted more by necessity than courtesy. It wasn't a
very abundant meal; during the Revolution food was scarce even
for those who, like my relatives, had a certain amount of money.
After dinner two of my older cousins decided to have an "Indian
wrestling" match. They sat down on opposite sides of a small
table; each grasped the other's right hand and tried to force his
opponent's arm to the table top. They were about evenly matched,
and they held the same position, red-faced and panting, for several
minutes. At last Edgardo won. "That doesn't prove a thing," Luis
said angrily. "You practice piano all day, and that's developed the
muscles in your wrist. But I bet you can't lift this kid with one
hand, like I can." Before I had a chance to escape he took me by
the seat of my trousers. The disaster that followed was horrible:
my cousin was left with a piece of my trousers in his hand and I
was left with a bare bottom. There in front of everybody, children
and adults, my secret was disclosed: I was wearing "nothing but
skin" under my suit. How humiliated I was! The boys laughed,
while the girls—some of them already young ladies—dropped
their eyes and blushed. At last my cousin María (the one who re-
minded me so of my mother because of her sad, frightfully myopic
eyes and her rather prominent teeth) took me tenderly by the
hand and led me into the next room. She made me remove my
trousers, put me into her bed, and proceeded to do her best to

mend them. It was not easy, for the cloth was so worn you could almost see through it.

It was a painful experience, but not an unrewarding one. It made my relatives aware of the state of poverty in which we were living, and brought a standing invitation for my brother and myself to have supper there every evening. For many months this was the only meal of the day we could count on.

This improved the situation immensely; but now, on the other hand, I had the problem of transportation. There were many days when I didn't have the streetcar fare, and it was a long, dreary walk from the Santa María district to Azcapotzalco at night, especially when it was raining.

During the day there was always the chance of being able to "hitch" a ride on the streetcar, at least part of the way. The second-class car, in which I traveled, was the second of the tandem; generally it was jammed, which favored my scheme. It called for a special technique, and in time I perfected it. Before getting aboard, you had to notice where the conductor was; if he was collecting fares at the front of the car, you hopped onto the platform at the rear and rode there until you saw him approaching. Then, at the first stop, or before if he was coming too fast, you dropped off and entered the car again at the front, trying not to be noticed. As the conductor moved through the car you kept behind him, keeping out of sight. If the two of you came face to face in the middle of the car, there was always the chance that he might assume you had been there all the time. If you were lucky enough to find a full streetcar, and were able to stay out of sight, the chances for a free trip were pretty good.

The ideal situation, though, was finding an empty seat and sliding into it when the conductor's back was turned. Usually he paid no attention to passengers who were already seated, assuming that

they had got on at the Zócalo and had paid their fares on his first round at the beginning of the line. This strategy—walking bravely into the car and coolly taking a seat—could be used only when you had the twenty centavos in your pocket. If you didn't, you had to remain on the platform, drop off as soon as you saw the conductor approaching, and make the rest of the trip on foot.

Needless to say, these little tricks were possible in those days only because automatic doors were not yet in use. With these, such as we have today, I would not have been able to get on and off while the car was in motion. Perhaps it was because of the nature of this maneuver that we called it "fly riding."

Sometimes, when it was very late or I was especially tired, I tried the "commuter" act. In this case, provided I had been able to find a seat, it was best to pretend to be asleep. If in spite of this the conductor asked for my fare, I would calmly say, "Commuter," hoping he would not ask to see my card. If this failed, I would search laboriously through every one of my pockets for the little piece of pasteboard that entitled the bearer to a month's unlimited transportation. With growing haste I would look first in my inside coat pockets, then proceed to the outside ones, and finally go through my trouser pockets. Sometimes it worked, and the conductor, genuinely convinced that I was a commuter who had forgotten his ticket, or perhaps merely feeling sorry for that skinny little boy with his pale, sorrowful face, would let me ride to the end of the line. More often than not, however, it didn't work; then I had to get off, ears red with humiliation and holding back the tears, under the stares of the other passengers, who knew perfectly well I had not forgotten anything and probably put me down as a shameless young scoundrel.

But even with bad luck I almost always gained something. Generally I was able to get as far as Tacuba, from where the hike to Azcapotzalco and then to Coachilco was not so bad— provided it wasn't raining. If it was, the pieces of cardboard I had put in my worn-out shoes became water-soaked and dissolved, and I concluded the journey with the naked soles of my feet in the mud.

I could feel my schoolmates' antagonism from the very first day. At the beginning it was a vague, uneasy feeling that was hard to describe or even substantiate; but the hostility in the air was not long in manifesting itself in tangible ways. The first of these demonstrations took place a few days after my enrollment.

The classes were held in two separate buildings, one on either side of Tepanecos Street. We met in the morning before school in the patio of one of these, and then marched across the street in single file to our classrooms in the other. We were crossing over as usual that morning when the boy in front of me, taking advantage of the fact that the teacher had preceded us into the other building, stepped to one side, put out his foot, and tripped me. I was furious —not so much at finding myself on the ground as at the general delight, evinced by the muffled laughter and giggling about me. I got to my feet without a word, brushing the dust from my coat and trousers and rubbing my hands where they had been skinned in the gravel. I went to my seat in the first row and tried to forget the incident.

This period of peace did not last long, however. The teacher was writing the names of the capitals of the states on the blackboard and I was copying them carefully, when suddenly some small, damp object stung my right ear. I saw the missile lying on my desk: a piece of orange peel. I turned quickly, just in time to see Antonio firing another piece at me with a slingshot from the fourth row. I ducked, none too soon. The giggling throughout the room made the teacher turn his head, but he didn't notice anything. As soon as I could I turned around again and showed Antonio the palm of my right hand, a gesture that said, "You'll pay for that!" He replied by holding his fist against his nose to indicate that he would break that member for me, and smiled in a self-assured way.

His confidence was not unwarranted. He was several years older than I, tall and strong, and a country boy used to hard work. If I were rash enough to fight him, there could be no doubt as to the outcome. I had never liked this overgrown lad with his thick lips and low forehead; he was a foul-mouthed bully. Now I saw that the dislike was probably mutual.

How could I get even? It occurred to me, of course, that I could report him to the teacher; but that would make me a "squealer," and my fellow students would hate me forever. No, this was a problem I had to solve myself.

I had never faced a difficult situation like this before. In the Florencio my trouble had been with the teacher, while my relations with my classmates had been excellent. They had admired my acts of rebellion and been amused by my clowning. Now it was the other way around. My teacher had shown a liking for me from the very moment my father had brought me to be enrolled, and my tractable and studious nature had endeared me to him even more. If I "squealed" he would probably take my side and punish Antonio; but I would be incurring the other boys' hostility and perhaps even the "ice treatment." On the other hand, the prospect of carrying out my threat to fight Antonio quite frankly terrified me. I would not only get hurt, but I would be made to look ridiculous. After considering all these aspects, I decided to confront my enemy not with force, where I knew I would be lost, but with words—a field in which I felt I was Antonio's superior. I would have to make him ashamed of himself, I reflected; I would have to make him feel like a coward.

By recess time my apprehension was all but unbearable. Doing my best to hide my fear, I went up to Antonio and, in a voice I tried to keep from trembling, I said loudly enough for the others to hear, "You big bully, pick on somebody your own size, instead of kids that are smaller than you!" Antonio regarded me with his little brown animal-like eyes, and retorted, "Shut up, you little snot-nose. If you weren't such a runt I'd smash your face for you." He turned his back on me and went to join some other boys who were playing leapfrog. He had backed down, and I considered it a victory. But my triumph was short-lived. No sooner had I taken my seat after recess than the attack was taken up again; only this time I was pelted not with orange peel but pepper tree berries. Whenever the teacher turned his back to point out something on the map, not only Antonio but several other boys peppered my head and neck with the little purple balls, fired from peashooters.

All morning I dreaded the moment when school let out. What would they do to me? How could I defend myself? And what had I ever done to them? I wanted to be friends. What did they have against me? However, nothing happened. I was allowed to go home for lunch unmolested. They ignored me when we came back to school at three, too. But when we were let out at five o'clock and I was hoping to slip away without being noticed, several boys blocked my way outside the door. "What do you want?" I asked them. Antonio, who was among them, said, "We're going to cure you of being such a big-mouth." "Oh, sure!" I began, intending to pursue my tactic of verbal defense, "All of you against . . ." He interrupted me with, "Here's somebody your own size," and pushed a boy of my age and height toward me. It was Jorge, who occupied the seat next to me.

At first I thought of asking why I should fight him: he had done nothing to me, and I rather liked him. Besides, it was obvious that he had no desire to fight me, either. But I saw there was no way out of it.

"Let's get away from here," somebody said. "Out in the open," another boy added.

No one said a word as we left the village and walked down a narrow dirt road with irrigation ditches on either side and fields of alfalfa beyond. The ditches were shallow and covered with algae, which gave off a strong odor of rotting vegetation.

"This is all right," said Antonio. Jorge and I faced each other with our hands in the guard position we had seen professional fighters assume in photographs. "You hit me first," Jorge said. "No, you first," I said. We were both afraid. My mouth felt dry, and my heart was hammering. Besides, the idea of striking a friend was very repugnant to me.

"Cowards! Sissies! You're both chicken!" our impatient schoolmates shouted, standing in a ring around us and pushing us toward each other. At last I was forced to fall against Jorge, and he replied with a wild swing. The battle was on. We began by exchanging clumsy and rather gentle blows, but gradually, as they became more painful, we got angry. Each punch elicited others in reply, and the harder the blow the more rapidly fell those that followed. We were no longer concerned with protecting ourselves, and had forgotten all about keeping our famous "guard" up. The one who was being attacked merely held his arms in front of his face until the blows stopped coming, and then the process was reversed. All fear had been forgotten. We were like a pair of furious, aggressive animals. We had become enemies in earnest.

I have no idea how long this had gone on when I was lucky enough to hit Jorge squarely on the nose. "That got the catsup running!" somebody cried. I turned to see who it was, and my opponent took advantage of my momentary distraction to land a blow on my mouth. I tasted blood, and flew at him with my eyes closed. We exchanged punches until I began seeing stars. Then we clinched, fell to the ground, and rolled over and over, still lashing out.

"That's enough," somebody said. "It's a draw." Antonio came up to me and regarded the blood trickling from my mouth. "You see? Now you've learned to keep your big mouth shut. You're going to have a shiner tomorrow."

We went back to Azcapotzalco exhausted, filthy, and happy. As we parted in the town square Jorge and I shook hands. Neither of us had lost, and neither had been a coward. We would be friends.

I walked slowly toward Coachilco. One eye was oozing, and I still tasted blood; but I was content. It was my first fight. There were many others to follow during my two years at Tepanecos, but I knew instinctively that this was the one that had opened wide the doors of friendship.

The Republic Prize

There was still, however, an invisible barrier between me and most of my classmates. Ironically enough, this was due to my reputation as a "rich kid," which persisted in spite of the fact that I often went hungry and had humiliating experiences because of our extreme poverty. This misconception almost made me lose, two years later, the only popular election I ever competed in.

This is how it happened. The revolutionary government, which had just been formed as a *de facto* regime, had set up a scholarship called "The Republic Prize" for the best student—in the eyes of his fellow pupils—among the primary school graduates of that year. The prize had a dual purpose: it was meant to acquaint young people with the new democratic processes that the Revolution wished to introduce into national politics, and was aimed at encouraging boys who had finished their schooling to go into agriculture. For the first time Mexico was becoming aware of the pressing need for a corps of technical experts in crop production. The project had been conceived by the engineer Félix Fulgencio Palavicini, who was at the time in charge of public education. It called for the awarding of a scholarship of fifty pesos a month and free tuition at the National School of Agriculture, where the recipient would study for a degree in agronomics. The competition was to be held in every school in the country, and the prize awarded to the boy who, having achieved high marks in his sixth year, was elected by secret ballot as the most deserving.

Our teacher (whom we called "El Tato" behind his back because he always carried a cane made from the reed known as *otate,* with which he threatened us but which he never used) explained the matter carefully. He spoke slowly, as though he were very tired—perhaps because of the tuberculosis which was already sapping his strength and was to carry him to his grave a few years later. After describing the benefits of the prize, he outlined the process of holding an election.

My heart skipped a beat.

I was about to complete my primary schooling, and lived in dread of finding myself unable to continue my studies; it was becoming increasingly obvious that I would have to get a job in order to help out at home. It was my great ambition, systematically encouraged by my father, to study law. Jarano held it to be the best and noblest of professions, and thought I was magnificently suited for it. I had never stopped to wonder whether or not he was right; I simply accepted without question that it would

be my career, and that there could be no doubt of my success. But we were now living in such misery that it seemed more and more likely that I would have to quit school. In the face of this threat, becoming an agronomic engineer struck me as quite acceptable. At least I would have a profession. I saw it as a plank that had come floating by to save me from the shipwreck of my life. There was always the chance that I could study law later.

With all the maturity of a boy just turned twelve, I had not the slightest doubt in my mind as to who deserved that prize. My grades were the highest in the class, and I burned with the ambition to be somebody. These were, in my callow eyes, more than sufficient reasons to be awarded the scholarship.

As my mind filled with visions of my future life, in which I saw myself dressed in denim behind the plow, healthy and suntanned, or tending domestic animals, or pruning fruit trees, our teacher began passing out blank slips of paper. On these we were to write the name of the boy we thought should be given the prize.

There was another excellent student in our class: a lad named Pedro, whose father owned a small dairy farm near Azcapotzalco. We were competitors not only for the first place in class work, but for the marble championship; we played in the street, all the way from school to the town square in Azcapotzalco. This needy, hardworking country boy was—I reflect *a posteriori*—undoubtedly a more suitable candidate than I for a scholarship at the National School of Agriculture. And yet I didn't think he had a chance against me in the election. I was so sure of winning that, although I was perfectly free to vote for myself, it was easy to show my impartiality by writing his name on my ballot and calmly tossing it into the wooden box at the front of the room.

Even so, during the tense moments that followed I awaited the outcome with great anxiety. My hands were sweating and I was embarrassed because my friends kept looking at me, many of them conveying by gestures, grins, or funny faces that they had voted for me.

After the counting of the votes, which was carried out with all the proper formalities under the watchful eye of the teacher and two witnesses, the results were announced: fifteen for Pedro, fifteen for me. I was so disappointed that I still don't know how I kept from bursting into tears. Since I was incapable of comprehending my schoolmates' real motives for voting as they had, the outcome struck me not only as unfair but as insulting. How could Pedro's situation be compared with mine? He didn't aspire to a professional career as I did, nor did he have my enormous ambition to distinguish myself and become a person of importance. And how could his need be thought to equal mine? His father owned those beautiful black and white cows I saw every evening, slowly returning to the stable with their udders swollen with milk; while in my house that commodity was a real luxury. I realized, too late, that my gentlemanly gesture of voting for my opponent —which had been wasted, since no one knew of it—had been a mistake. If I had cast a vote for myself (which I had a perfect right to do, and which Pedro had undoubtedly done) I would have won, if only by one vote.

As these thoughts passed through my mind I sat with a lump in my throat, keeping my eyes on my desk to avoid my classmates' glances and trying not to cry. The teacher announced that since there had been a tie we would take another vote. We were allowed ten minutes to talk it over among ourselves. It was then that I learned why some of them had voted against me. They told me openly, almost brutally: I was a "little gentleman," an "outsider," a rich boy; we owned our own house in Coachilco, and my father was a lawyer. I didn't need a scholarship. When I grew

up I would go to live in the city. What did I know about farm-
ing? Pedro, on the other hand, was poor and had grown up in
the country. Although they didn't say as much, they made it quite
clear that Pedro was one of their own kind, a country boy like
themselves, while they looked upon me as a strange creature with
light-colored eyes, whose ways were different from theirs. I suppose they thought that in one way or another I would be able to
get the money for an education—after all, I was not a *ladino**
for nothing!—while for Pedro it would not be so easy.

How could I make them see the humiliating conditions—which
I was instinctively trying to improve—under which I lived? How
could I explain that my need was greater, that this scholarship
was the answer to my never-ending prayers (which an impious
child brought up in secular schools and bereft of his mother had
never put into words)? Besides, I had too much pride to plead,
like a beggar, for the one vote that I felt was my just and obvious
due.

Nevertheless, I did my best to explain what my life was really
like. I pointed out that although my father was a lawyer, he had
earned no fees for a long time; in those troubled days the courts
functioned only sporadically, and at the moment were not even
open. I confessed ashamedly that my father had not been able to
get any steady work, and only substituted from time to time at
night as a collector of conductors' receipts for the streetcar company. They could see for themselves how badly our house needed
repairs. The paint and plaster were peeling, and you could see
the adobe bricks underneath; in some places we had boards cover-
ing the broken windows; it was mortgaged, and we couldn't even

---

* *Ladino* is a term used by the Indians. It refers, in a general way, to
anyone of European stock or with some non-Indian blood, and carries
overtones of duplicity and cunning. *Tr.*

pay the interest on the 1600-peso loan; we had not been evicted only because the courts were closed. I concluded by reminding them that I "boarded" at Doña Lucha's—whose miserable little restaurant was also a charcoal and pulque shop, as some of them knew—in company with Don Pancho, the tremendously powerful town blacksmith who was so good at shoeing horses, and the burro drivers who occasionally stopped in Azcapotzalco on their way to the city. I added that I had not dared show my face there since last week, because I didn't have the money to pay her bill. I told them they could ask the fifth-grade teacher if they didn't believe me; he, too, was one of Doña Lucha's customers. With all this I tried to show my schoolmates that although I had light-colored eyes and chestnut hair, my shoes were shined, and my suit was made of wool, I was by no means in easy circumstances.

Did these Indian boys understand what I was trying to tell them? Did they feel my dire necessity? Or was it, perhaps, the lump in my throat and my tight voice that conveyed my anguish and made them see that the Prize meant more to me than to Pedro? I don't know. But the fact is that when we took the second vote, to choose one or the other of the two candidates, the outcome was astounding: twenty-nine for me and one for Pedro.

I went home full of dreams and plans. My future was assured. My name and picture, with the story of my victory, would appear in all the newspapers. Soon I would be well known, and one day I would be famous! Now I had two problems: I must provide two photographs to accompany the official declaration of my election and the notice to the press, and I had to find some way to get hold of the papers so I could enjoy reading the story. My father solved the first—not without some sacrifice—by giving me fifty centavos. (I might say in passing that he was not as delighted at my triumph as I was.) This was the price of three pass-port-size photographs at the studio on Azcapotzalco's main street. Now I had only to get the papers. I made arrangements with Don Pepe, the Spaniard who ran the grocery store on the little plaza in Coachilco, to let me see them when they came. He kindly agreed not only to save them for me, but to go through *El Universal* personally. It would be sure to carry the story of my resounding victory, for I had been assured that it would appear in every daily in the Capital.

I scanned the papers assiduously for days, weeks, months—but in vain. They were full of news of skirmishes between the government forces and the "rebels," and of the fighting in Europe between the Germans and the Allies, which I read avidly, trying to follow what was happening. Occasionally I would come across a few lines, usually with a photograph, about the winner of one of these elections in some other school; but not one word ever appeared about the celebrated Republic Prize competition at the Vicente Alcaraz School in Azcapotzalco.

Neither I nor the school ever received any official notice awarding me the scholarship. I went to see the principal several times to make sure that he had notified the authorities; at last, feeling sorry for me or simply bored by my insistence, he gave me copies of the letter he had sent to the Department of Education and the press release.

After a time there was a change in the political situation. The engineer Palavicini gave up his government post to take over the editorship of one of the larger daily papers. No one any longer cared, or even remembered, about the Republic Prize. At night, by the light of my kerosene student lamp, I read and reread the Vicente Alcaraz School's official statement of my election, feeling very bitter and trying to think of some way of getting that scholarship. For a while I considered going to see Palavicini at his newspaper office, in the hope that he, at least, would remember the project he had initiated and that he had enough influence with his successors in the government to see that his laudable program was carried out. But I never found the courage.

It was not until many years later—I was Secretary of the Treasury at the time—that I met Palavicini at a party at his son Manuel's house and took the opportunity to tell him the sad and curious story of my failure to receive the Republic Prize in spite of my democratic victory. Several of my old school friends were there that evening, and we were chatting after dinner. Someone pointed out that my life would have been very different if the government had kept its word. Another member of the group replied that it would have made no difference at all: it was common knowledge that the School of Agriculture prepared as many young men for politics as did the School of Law.

At that time I was being spoken of as a possible candidate for President of the Republic in the coming elections; Palavicini had returned to newspaper work after several years in the diplomatic field, and was now also a radio commentator on international events. He looked at me with those blue eyes that sparkled with vitality and humor in spite of his sixty-odd years and said, "I predict better luck for you in the coming election, my friend. But if you lose the prize this time, it won't be through any fault of mine." Everyone laughed, and I was a little embarrassed. I didn't know quite how to answer, not wanting to say anything that might be misinterpreted at that crucial point in my political career.

"La Cucaracha"

It was 1914.

There were two contending factions of Mexican revolutionaries, each claiming to be the true champion of the authentic principles of the glorious Revolution of 1910. They had met face to face at the Convention of Aguascalientes: the followers of Carranza on one side, those of Zapata and Villa on the other.

Mexico City, at the moment in the hands of the Conventionists, was, naturally, one of the most hotly disputed military objectives. And yet there was never any fighting within the city itself; because of the difficulties in defending it—or perhaps for political reasons—it was simply abandoned by the withdrawing forces whenever the other army took it over.

By this time the residents of the Capital were used to seeing the troops of either faction parading through the streets, usually on horseback; they were no longer surprised at the huge charro hats, often adorned with pictures of the Virgin or of the saints, that identified the armies of the south, or the "Stetsons" worn by the "armed citizens" from the north.

The horses and men fascinated me: the former because of the love I have always felt for them, and the urge to ride one, even for a moment—a desire I was sometimes able to satisfy after pleading again and again with some soldier; and the latter because I enjoyed talking with these people who seemed to come from another world. Their different ways of dressing and speaking awoke in me an indefinable romantic interest in the places they came from, and a resolve to visit those parts of our country one day. Whenever I could, I engaged one of them in conversation—whether he was a soldier or an officer, and regardless of which party he belonged to—while he was tightening his cinch or feeding and watering his horse at the curb.

The relative calm with which the city was successively taken and retaken made it hard at times to know just who was occupying it at any given moment. One was often disagreeably surprised to find that the money he had in his pocket was worthless; when he went to buy something, he was informed that Villa's "bed sheets" were no longer any good, or that Carranza's *bilimbiques** were no longer being accepted.

---

* A contemptuous term for fiduciary paper money issued during the Revolution. Its etymology is uncertain, but one hypothesis has it that the word is a corruption of "William Vique." Vique, it is said, was paymaster for an hacienda in the state of Durango, and paid the workers in his own

Another common annoyance was the breakdown of public services, principally the streetcars. There were no buses or other means of transportation in those days, and this meant a long walk from school in the Roma district to our house in the suburbs of Azcapotzalco. Getting to school in the morning didn't worry me: when the streetcars weren't running, I simply didn't go.

But in spite of these inconveniences life went on in a much more orderly fashion than one might have expected. The populace has an astounding capacity for adapting itself to any situation, no matter how difficult.

On one of these occasions when one army was entering the city and another was withdrawing, I had an experience that made a profound impression on me.

I was in my first year at the National Preparatory School. My classes were held, not in the old building on San Ildefonso, but in a more modern one on the Plaza de Miravalle, in the Roma district. It was called "the Boarding School," no doubt because it was on the site of a former federal institution of that name. Among the students, however, it was known as "the Doghouse," in view of the fact that first-year pupils were nicknamed "dogs." We were sent to this building for two reasons: there was no room for us in the main building, and the government was beginning to consider setting up what later were to be known as "secondary schools." These were to bridge the gap between primary school, with its regime of absolute control and strict discipline, and preparatory school, where the students enjoyed almost complete freedom.

------

scrip. These notes were known locally as *vales* (IOU's) *de Bilimbique*. When Pancho Villa's money came into circulation in that area, and Vique turned to using it to pay his men, the name passed from the scrip to the currency. *Tr.*

I had been terribly disappointed to find that I could not attend classes in the old, impressive colonial building. At thirteen, I already felt like a real university student, and was naturally attracted by the free and easy behavior and speech of the young men who were enrolled there. I had got to know some of them in Professor Alejandro Quijano's Spanish language class, where my brother had taken me as an auditor several Saturdays.

That afternoon the streets teemed with soldiers, some on foot and some on horseback, moving fast and looking worried. There were no streetcars running, as usual. When I came out of "the Doghouse" after my last class, I had resigned myself to the long walk home. By the time I reached the San Rafael area it was getting dark, and I began to consider spending the night with my cousins the Carreras, who lived nearby. I turned left at the corner of Santa María La Ribera and Gabino Barreda streets, and soon found myself at the street door I knew so well; I had lived in that house for several years, until my mother sold it to one of her sisters at my grandmother's death.

My aunt and uncle greeted me with their usual cordiality and affection; but I soon saw that they would not be able to put me up for the night. They had guests: a mother and her two daughters, distant relatives of my uncle's, who were fleeing the revolutionary armies. They planned to stay there indefinitely. As soon as I realized the situation I tried to take my leave, on some pretext or other. But my aunt, who was quite aware that if I didn't have supper with them I wouldn't eat that night, insisted that I join them at the table—even though one more mouth created a problem. Feeding her family was hard enough in normal times, and more difficult now that even staples were not easy to come by. With the utmost good will and that affection that is found only in large and closely united families, as ours had been, she made me share their meal: watered-down boiled beans, bread made of lima bean flour (wheat flour was unobtainable), and *café con leche* that contained none of the first and little of the second (it was made from roasted chick-peas, which gave it the appearance but not the taste of coffee, diluted with thin, bluish milk, and sweetened with raw brown sugar). But the good-humored conversation made us forget the shortages, our hunger, and even the political situation—which at my age seemed unimportant, anyway.

It was nearly ten o'clock when I got up to leave. My aunt regarded me with those small, deep-set, kindly, sad eyes of hers and said, "My child, I hate to let you leave at this time of night in these troubled times; but you can see for yourself—there just isn't any room!"

I thanked her, and boasted that I would be in no danger whatsoever; I was used to walking alone at any hour of the day or night. Secretly, however, I was not looking forward at all to that long hike, and in spite of my cockiness I was pretty scared. Nor was I at all eager to get home, where there was no one to welcome me. (My mother had died, my brother—barely sixteen—was in the army, and my father worked at night.)

I set off in the direction of Tlaxpana, which was then still like a kind of checkpoint at the entrance to the city, and crossed the bridge over the Consulado River. I walked fast, following the streetcar line, meeting no one along the long, almost unpopulated route. As I entered Tacuba I noticed that the streets were unusually empty, and I became more and more apprehensive. There was not a single electric light burning, and only the yellow glow from a few windows, reflected in little rectangles on the cobblestones, relieved the blackness of the night. When I turned onto the highway leading from Tacuba to Azcapotzalco, the thick trees bordering the main avenue of the Imparcial district only made everything seem gloomier. I kept to the middle of the road, where it was not quite so dark, and began walking faster; but some inner force seemed to be holding me back, and I was tempted to turn around. I decided that that would be pointless, and went on, a little more slowly, trying to make out the houses that lined both sides of the street. They were typical of those built at the turn of the century, set apart and with little gardens; behind their ivy-covered iron fences or high walls, which lent them a certain manorial air, they aspired to a kind of elegance.

It must have been a quarter of an hour after leaving Tacuba when I met a man coming from the opposite direction, moving very fast. He shot out from the shadows so suddenly that he seemed to have materialized out of thin air. I was terrified, but I gathered the courage to stop him and ask if anything was wrong; he looked like a man running away from something.

"Anything wrong!" he said. "Just that the Carranza troops are coming—or maybe they're leaving, I don't know. Anyway, there are soldiers up ahead."

Without another word he set off again, almost running. I suppose he thought he had told me all I needed to know.

Again I considered turning back, more seriously this time. Where could I spend the night? True, I had some relatives in Santa María La Ribera, but they were in no position to put me up, either; besides, it would be after midnight when I reached their house on Rosa Street. So I took heart and went on, telling myself that nothing was going to happen to a mere boy. I regretted that I was not armed, in the innocent belief that if I were I would be able to defend myself. To avoid being taken unawares again, I got out of the street and walked along in the shadows under the trees. I would be able to see anyone coming toward me, and could not easily be seen myself, for I was dressed in mourning for my mother. About ten minutes later I saw something glisten among the trees, which I correctly identified as a rifle barrel. A voice called out, "Halt! Who goes there?"

I stood rooted to the spot, not knowing what to answer. The voice came again, louder and menacing: "God damn it! Who goes there? Answer, or I'll fire!"

From some part of my subconscious sprang the reply I should make in a case like this; but at the same time a terrifying thought came to my mind: suppose they weren't really Carrancistas after all? A mistake could be fatal.

"*Viva México!*" I cried as loud as I could, taking no chances. "I'm a peaceful citizen!"

"All right, advance—but slow, with your hands up!"

I obeyed. When I had taken a few steps I saw a soldier who had been hidden in a doorway, obviously a sentry; from the smell of his breath it was equally obvious that he was drunk. As I approached he said to someone standing beside him in the darkness, "Hey, gimme a match. Let's light the lantern and have a look at this guy's face."

A light flared in the doorway, and a kerosene lantern was held up to my face. Although I was partially blinded by the flame, I could see that they both carried rifles and wore crossed cartridge belts filled with ammunition.

"Well, look what we found," one of them said. "What d'you suppose he is?"

He looked me up and down, undoubtedly surprised to see a youngster in short pants.

"Suppose we ask him," the other replied. "What're you doing here?"

He had addressed me as *tu,* which offended me more than his tone of voice. I was at that age when one no longer thinks of himself as a child, although he knows perfectly well that he is not yet a man; it didn't occur to me that he had used the familiar form because I was only a boy. I felt that he was speaking to me as though to an inferior, and my dignity was wounded.

"I'm on my way home," I said angrily.

"At this time of night?" demanded the first soldier, in a tone of mockery and disbelief. I didn't answer. "At your age?" he added.

His questions were like a slap in the face. Although I was frightened, I refused to admit that he had any right to treat me like a child. I decided to get even by refusing to say another word.

"Oho, you don't want to talk, eh?" he said after a moment. "All right—get moving."

He gave me a shove that left no doubt as to what he wanted me to do or the direction I was to take. After walking some three hundred yards in silence, we came to the best house in the district. It was remarkable for its size and its spacious grounds, and had been pointed out to me by my father as the residence of the aged and distinguished journalist Reyes Spíndola. Two sentries were posted at the gate, and in the garden surrounding the house I could make out a great many men wrapped in sarapes, sleeping among the trees. Beyond them were some shadowy forms I later identified as horses.

I marched along before my captors, trying to move with some dignity; to ease my mind I kept telling myself that I could easily get out of this predicament by simply speaking to the officer in charge and identifying myself as a peaceful student. With this idea in mind I went up to one of the sentries at the gate and demanded, "Who's in charge here?"

Instead of answering, the soldier gripped his 30-30 and called out in a loud voice, "Corporal of the guard!"

At these words a man wrapped in a sarape, wearing no hat, came over to us; it was obvious that he had been asleep on the lawn.

"What's up?" he asked, looking at me.

Before I could answer, one of the soldiers who had brought me said, "We found him sneaking around in the trees. He won't talk."

"That's not true," I cried angrily. "This man is lying!"

With no change of expression the corporal gave me a blow on the head with his open hand; it didn't really hurt, but it knocked off my hat.

"Shut up, you!" he said. "Take him to the Major."

They shoved me up the front steps. A soldier standing guard opened the door, and in the entrance hall beyond I could see several men seated at a table in the light of an oil lamp. As I recall, they were playing cards and drinking—or perhaps just talking.

"Major," said the soldier who had captured me, "here's somebody for you. I think he's a spy or something. He says he's on his way home, and then when we get him here he gets tough with the corporal."

One of the men got up, took his Stetson from the table, put it on, carefully shaped the brim with both hands, and walked over to us. He wore a green gabardine shirt and riding trousers of a darker shade, and kept slapping his boot with a swagger stick. He examined me with eyes that seemed very blue against his sunburned face.

"So—we don't want to talk, eh?"

I was growing more terrified every minute.

"I have nothing to tell, my Colonel," I said in a voice that didn't seem to belong to me. I had heard the soldier address him as "Major," and I could see the star on his hat; but I wanted to flatter him. I went on hurriedly: "I'm a student, and I was on my way home. I live in Azcapotzalco. I was on foot because the streetcars aren't running. What more can I say?"

"Where're the enemy troops?"

"I don't know." By this time I was feeling genuine panic.

"I think you do know. I think you're working for that son of a bitch General Genovevo de la O. You're hanging around to see what you can see, and then you're going back and spill it."

"That's not true," I answered with a knot in my throat. "I don't know that Señor General."

"What d'you mean, 'that *Señor General*'! You're pretty damned respectful toward that bastard." He seemed to think it over for a moment, and then said, "If you're a civilian, why did you call me 'my Colonel'?"

"Because I have a brother in the army, and I've always heard him speak to his officers that way."

"In which army?" he barked. Now he seemed openly interested in what I was saying. I reflected that I didn't know for sure which party this outfit belonged to. I would have to take a chance. If I was wrong it would be the end of me. I hesitated, but not for long. The Stetson gave me the clue. I replied as calmly as I could, "What other army could it be, my Colonel? The Constitution-alists."

I saw immediately that I had guessed right, but the Major still seemed unconvinced of my innocence.

"What's his outfit?"

I answered promptly.

"He's under General González—Manuel W. González, the Third Brigade. He's a second lieutenant."

During my interrogation, the other men at the table—who

were no doubt also officers—had gotten to their feet. One of them took pity on my small figure, probably knowing from the sound of my voice that I was doing my best not to cry. He spoke up.

"Leave the poor little kid alone, Pepe. Let him go on home."

This show of sympathy broke down the last of my resistance, and I could no longer hold back the tears. I stood there ashamed, head down, hiding my face.

"All right," said the Major. "We'll let him go. But first he has to dance 'La Cucaracha' for us."

This solution seemed to satisfy everybody, and there was a general movement toward the door. I gathered from this that the dancing was to take place in the garden. When we were near the fountain by the front steps, the Major said, "This is fine."

They gathered in a ring about me, and someone began to sing:

> The cockroach, the cockroach
> Can't march another step . . .

I stood there without moving. My tears had dried by now, and I was filled with a terrible wrath. Although I was still frightened, I felt that I was being made a fool of, and resolved that I would not be a plaything for these men.

"Can't you hear?" the Major shouted. "Dance!"

"I don't know how," I said in a low voice, but firmly.

"I'll show you how, you dumb little brat!"

As he said this the Major took a rifle from one of the men. The barrel of the 30–30 gleamed in the glow of an oil lamp, and the dry sound of the bolt made my stomach tighten.

"Are you going to dance, or aren't you?" he said, lowering the rifle and taking careful aim at one of my feet, at the same time motioning with his head for the others to step out of the line of fire. They quickly moved aside, and I was left standing by myself.

For an endless moment I remained motionless—not out of bravado, but waiting for the music. The Major fired. I felt the flash on my face, and the bullet hit the pavement an inch or two from my right foot, drawing sparks and whistling away into the darkness. I lifted that foot at once, and began hopping from one to the other, without rhythm or sense. It wasn't a dance or anything resembling one, and in the absence of music or meter it must have been comical and absurd. Soon the soldiers were laughing and calling out to each other.

"Just look at that! What a good dancer he is!"

I still wore short pants and black lisle stockings. My thin legs drew the attention of one of the men.

"You know what he looks like, pal? A sea gull!"

I was beginning to get tired. My little hops grew smaller and smaller, until they were no more than symbolic. The men called out, "More! More!"

Someone in the group, inspired by the shouting and my ridiculous dance, began to sing at the top of his voice:

> The cockroach, the cockroach
> Can't march another step
> Because he's gone and smoked
> His marihuana up.

Other voices joined in the shrieking chorus. When they died away I stopped hopping.

"No! More!" they howled. "Sing some more, Juan, so he can dance!"

Then the first voice began again, loud and out of tune:

> There go the Carrancistas,
> They're off for Sombrerete
> To deliver a kick in the ass
> To General Navarrete.

The chorus chimed in:

> The cockroach, the cockroach . . .

The enthusiasm was mounting steadily. I kept dancing, driven on by the singing and by the memory of that rifle shot; I never took my eyes off the weapon, which the Major was still aiming at my feet.

When the chorus ended the solo voice went on:

> The Christmas parties are over,
> No more cinnamon rolls;
> So bring on all the whores
> And let them lick my balls.

And then the others shrieked:

> The cockroach, the cockroach . . .

They were having a marvelous time, but my little leaps were beginning to exhaust me. At last I stopped.

"I can't dance any more," I said. "Please, Sir, I haven't any strength left."

The Major smiled and pulled the trigger. I don't know how close the bullet came that time, and I didn't hear the ricochet. In the uproar and my own panic I couldn't distinguish anything. I instinctively began skipping again, with renewed energy. I don't know how long that torture went on, with the singing, the roars of laughter, the shots. Whenever I stopped, there came another flash from the rifle, and the voices rose again.

Happily, everything in this world becomes boring after a while. The soloist ran out of lyrics, and with each repetition of the old ones he was less of a success. Besides, I was really exhausted by this time, able to lift my feet only an inch or so from the ground, and probably my dance was not funny any more. Enthusiasm was waning. I had just begun to think that they were going to give me a rest when an officer came up and said something in a low voice to the Major. He forgot about me at once and began issuing orders to the men. I suppose they had been ordered to advance on Mexico City. There was a general dispersion, with men running to get their horses from behind the house, tightening cinches, and putting on bridles.

I was left standing there, not knowing what to do. I could hardly believe that I was still alive. It was like waking from a nightmare.

"Beat it, stupid!" someone called as he passed me. It was the officer who had come to my defense; he was leading a small horse whose saddle was hung with so many objects that I couldn't see how he was going to mount. Nobody stopped me as I went out the gate. I wanted to run, but I was afraid of calling attention to myself. I walked away as fast as my weary legs would carry me.

On my way to Azcapotzalco I met several groups of soldiers; some were in formation, while others were moving in no order at all. Some were on foot and some were on horseback. They advanced silently, seeming to be in no hurry; it was easy to see that these were not troops going into combat. The pleasures and comforts of Mexico City awaited them, but they betrayed no eagerness. Perhaps they were too tired. At each new encounter my heart skipped a beat, but luckily no one paid any further attention to me.

When I reached our house in Coachilco it was getting light. I opened the big old door with an enormous key I carried in my pocket and went into the shadows of the dirty, empty, lonely house.

Veracruz

I was excited at the prospect of the trip. All journeys, any journey, had a special charm for me in those days. Besides, going to Veracruz meant watching the ships come in, and seeing the loading and unloading of cargo on the piers; picking up shells along the beach; swimming in the sea; sniffing the ocean breeze; and, in short, discovering a whole new world.

It was my uncle Alfonso who had suggested the trip. We must take advantage, he said, of the happy coincidence of his brother Manuel's stay in Veracruz with my summer vacation from school. A holiday at the seaport would be instructive and good for my health. My relatives worried a great deal about my persistent pallor, the circles under my eyes that made them look smaller and more deep-set than they actually were, and my inability to gain weight. They loved giving me advice and recommending tonics, every one of which would miraculously transform the skinny, sickly-looking lad that I was into a strong and splendid young man.

My father, however, received the invitation with very little enthusiasm; if he didn't openly reject it, it must have been because he felt that he had no right to deprive me of a pleasure that he was in no position to give me. My uncle had got me a pass on the railroad, and his brother Manuel would take care of my expenses in Veracruz.

I was delighted. I looked forward to the trip, of course, but there was another secret attraction. My uncle Manuel managed and acted in a vaudeville troupe that specialized in *zarzuelas*— the traditional short musical farces of the Spanish theater. If I stayed with him, I thought, I would have the chance to get a good look at the actresses, even if only the bit players. My imagination was inflamed, for in our house people who "trod the boards" were always said to have loose morals and free and easy ways. This had been one of the reasons for the coolness that existed between my mother's pseudoaristocratic family and my father's relatives, who made their living as best they could—legitimately, but with no great regard for society's prejudices. Some of them were in the theater.

In my mind I pictured the "vedettes'" dressing rooms, all curtains, cushions, and silks. I daydreamed of finding myself there in intimate conversation with one of those extraordinary women. I saw her putting on her make-up, combing her hair, dressing, undressing.

It was the summer of 1915. In those days the trip from the Capital to the Gulf of Mexico was not a simple matter. A little before this, Don Venustiano Carranza had withdrawn from Mexico City, which was considered militarily indefensible, and had taken refuge in Veracruz with his government to reorganize the Constitutional forces.

After defeating the southern army in several battles and taking Puebla, the Carrancistas had occupied Mexico City again, and communications between the Capital and the port of Veracruz were by this time almost back to normal. But the trains were still not running regularly; they were continually harrassed by Zapata's troops, so that Carranza was forced to employ large detachments of his army to keep the line open. Zapata was thus cooperating with Villa, who was engaged in a battle to the death with Obregón.

Earlier, Carranza had not hesitated to give up Mexico City without a struggle, but this time he was determined to hold it in the interests of international prestige. This was of prime importance at the moment, for it was imperative to convince the United States—which he ultimately did—to recognize his administration as the *de facto* government. This recognition was to be a determining factor in the Constitutionalists' triumph over the Villa and Zapata factions. But Carranza had to do more than merely claim that his party represented "law and order" and the will of the people, and that it was prepared to respect international commitments. He needed objective proof: the possession of Mexico City. Under these circumstances, keeping communications open between it and Veracruz—which the legalistically-minded First Executive had declared the Capital of the Republic—was absolutely essential.

With characteristic stubborness, Carranza tightened his hold on both capitals, and was to maintain them from then on; but he could not stop the Zapatistas from derailing and blowing up the trains. As a consequence there were frequent skirmishes and even open fighting along the Interoceanic and Mexican Line.

My father, who knew the situation, naturally winced at the thought of my taking such a journey; but in view of my insistence and his brother's assurances, he agreed to allow me a pleasure trip that was almost unheard-of in those turbulent times.

He and I arrived at the station very early in the morning. The train was not to leave until eight, but if you wanted a seat you had to get aboard almost at dawn. There was no other means of transportation, and very few trains were available. The whole country's rolling stock had been taken over by the armies—chiefly Villa's and Carranza's—for moving troops, horses, and cannon, and for the commanders' offices and quarters.

At that stage in the Revolution the trains were actually rolling barracks for the contending armies. Soldiers rode everywhere— not only inside the cars, but perched on the roofs and clinging to the rods beneath—for often the movement of troops from one part of the country to another was a matter of life or death. Whenever these trains loaded with soldiers, their families, horses, and impedimenta made a halt, they were immediately transformed into a military camp. Little nomadic villages sprang up around them, with even some primitive commerce; they were like the temporary settlements of wandering tribes.

I had no trouble finding a seat next to the window in the coach marked First Class; but soon other passengers began pouring in, and long before departure time the car was completely filled. Not only were all the seats taken, but people were standing in the aisles and in the vestibules. It was clear that the coach was more "mixto" than first class, and that its occupants had come prepared for any emergency. In appearance, in smell, and in the nature and number of the bundles they carried, they in no way resembled first class ticket holders. In addition to suitcases and hampers of all shapes and sizes, there were crates of chickens, bales of merchandise, and baskets and bags filled with food. By seven o'clock it was impossible to move and difficult to breathe, even though all the windows were open.

My father got off the train and stood on the platform by my window, giving me last-minute words of advice. Above all, I must never, for any reason, leave my seat; I would have no way of enforcing my rights as "first occupant," and would have to stand up for the rest of the trip. I must not eat any "slop" along the way: no candy, no snacks, no soft drinks. In the station where we would stop at noon I must buy (without moving from my seat) something "healthy" for lunch. The best thing would be a piece of chicken and a glass of milk—but only if the milk had been boiled. I must not allow myself to be seduced by the tempting aroma of enchiladas, sweet rolls, or fried meat; any of these could make me sick. I must think of the consequences of getting ill on a journey like this, with no one to take care of me; carelessness on my part could turn it into a real tragedy. Then, as though he had almost forgotten, he reached into his coat pocket and took out a ten-peso bill in "Veracruz money," carefully folded.

"This is all I have, but I think it'll see you through the trip. Once there, you won't have any problem. Manuel will give you whatever you need. You shouldn't have any trouble finding him."

He repeated his instructions. When I got to Veracruz I was to take the streetcar that passed right by the entrance of the railway station, and get off at the Eslava Theater, where my uncle's *zarzuela* company was playing. They were open cars, and I would be able to see everything on both sides of the street; even so, I had better ask the conductor to tell me when to get off. In the unlikely event that my uncle was not at the theater, they would tell me where to find him.

"He lives on one of the streets behind the theater. I can't remember if it's Juárez or Hidalgo, and I don't know the number; but, I repeat, they can tell you at the theater. He's sure to be there in the evening."

After a moment he added, "You should arrive tonight about eight. I hope you don't run into any trouble."

His detailed instructions and a certain tone in his voice showed that he was worried. After all, I was not even fourteen, and taking a pleasure trip was not the wisest or most commonplace thing to do at a time when revolutionary armies were locked in a bloody struggle for control of the country.

At last the conductor gave the third and final call, and the train began to move. My father took my hand briefly, and I could feel his love and concern in that touch. He was saying goodby not as to a child but as to a friend, as to a man setting out on an adventure. I was deeply moved, for I realized then that he had begun to regret his generosity, and would gladly have kept me from going if he could.

Once the train was in motion, our car began to fill up with passengers from the other coaches, where the crush was even greater. There was hardly any place to stand, and they were crowded together like cigarettes in a package. It was such a conglomerate mass that I couldn't see how the women and children who had no seats would be able to endure such discomfort for an entire day. They gradually settled down and made themselves as comfortable as possible. Some perched on bundles, some sat on the floor, and those who had only standing room leaned against the walls or the seats. Whenever the locomotive gave a sudden lurch—it seemed to be having trouble maintaining an even speed—they kept their balance by falling back against their neighbors.

Now that we were moving the air was better, and I began to feel more relaxed. The monotonous click-clack of the rails made a background for the crying of children, the voices of scolding mothers, and shouted conversations, and it all fused into a dull, meaningless roar.

I was overcome by a vague melancholy as the landscape of the Valley of Mexico passed before my eyes. It was a limpid August morning, as only those on the Central Plateau can be. The mountains in the distance, more blue than violet, seemed to have drawn closer. I could make out details in the terrain under an intensely luminous sun that bathed cornfields and farmers' huts and glared on the bleached earth near the railroad track. It was a cheery sun, not yet high enough to take away the coolness of the morning. Under the spell of my pleasant melancholy, I felt that I must engrave on my mind every feature of the scene before me, as though I were going away for a long time and might never see those familiar and beloved things again. My eagerness and excitement had completely disappeared. I was almost sorry that I had embarked on this adventure; now, remembering my father's expression and the pressure of his hand, I began to feel that it was somehow fraught with peril.

I decided to occupy my mind by reading the book I had brought with me. With some difficulty I stood up on my seat and reached for the suitcase my father had placed on the luggage rack above my head. In doing so I had to disturb my seatmate. She was a fat, middle-aged lady who kept leaning on me as she, in turn, was shoved by the people standing in the aisle.

My novel—a bon voyage gift from my cousin Laura—was

Pérez Galdós' *Marianela,* beautifully bound in red leather. As I read, however, I found that far from cheering me up, it only depressed me more. I was saddened by the story of that maimed and horribly ugly girl and her intense love for the blind man whom she served as guide. At the age of thirteen it was easy to be touched by her terrible dilemma: did she want him to regain his sight and cast her out when he saw that she was not the beauty he thought she was, or would she prefer that he spend the rest of his life in darkness, continuing to admire and need her? I put myself in her place, and felt my eyes well up with pity.

From time to time the train would come to an almost complete stop and then continue cautiously, as though the engineer were afraid of meeting some obstacle on the track. There were inexplicably long waits at tiny stations where no one seemed to be getting on or off.

It must have been about two in the afternoon, during one of these stops, when I decided to have some lunch. I have the impression that we were in Apizaco, but I'm not sure; I remember only that it seemed to be a station of some importance, and that a great many vendors were running along the platform on either side of the train, crying their wares.

"Get your *lonche* here, young man!" an Indian woman called out, holding up something in a basket covered with a napkin. I asked if she had any chicken, and, as she did, bought half a breast wrapped in three cold, stiff tortillas. Although I was hungry, I had to force the food down; the chicken, boiled God only knew how many hours before, was cold and tasteless, and the tortillas were damp. As I was still hungry, I ignored my father's warning and bought from another vendor some marvelous-looking enchiladas that were handed to me in a piece of brown wrapping paper. They were bright red, adorned with slices of raw onion, and sprinkled with grated cheese. They looked, smelled, and turned out to be delicious. From a barefoot, smiling lad carrying a glass pitcher filled with white liquid in one hand and a not very clean-looking glass in the other, I obtained what I thought was milk. It proved to be pulque. I completed my lunch with a slice of pineapple.

The train began to move again. I read for a while, until more stops gave me the opportunity to buy some cookies and candy. I counted my money and found that I had spent a good part of my ten-peso capital. I consoled myself with the thought that I wouldn't have to buy anything else for the rest of the trip, and settled down for a nap. Lulled by the motion and sound of the train, I slept for a long time. At dusk I was awakened by another halt. I could tell from the chilly mountain air that we had been climbing. A few of the passengers were pacing up and down impatiently along the roadbed, keeping close to the train. We were out in the country, and there was not a sound. Suddenly rifle shots came from the distance and echoed from the mountains. The women in the coach instinctively clutched their children, and the passengers who were outside boarded the train hurriedly.

After some time we began moving again, very slowly. The train crept along for half an hour, then came to a halt. Again we heard shots, from a deep valley on our right; they were answered by others, farther off. I asked my seat companion if she knew where we were and what was happening. She said that we were approaching the Del Macho pass and that a Zapatista party had stationed itself along the track to stop the train. She seemed extraordinarily calm, as though she were discussing something very unimportant. Once we had fallen into conversation she never stopped talking. Thus I learned that she was a merchant who made frequent trips bringing goods from Mexico City to Veracruz, which had become a very good market because of the increase in population that had taken place following the establishment of the Constitutionalist government.

"We're going to run into trouble," she told me serenely. "Once these things start, you never know how they're going to end, or when. My last trip to the Capital, last month, took us three days. The Zapatistas put a bomb on the track and blew up the locomotive. Fortunately, the train was going very slow, and nobody was killed but the engineer and the fireman. But after that there was a battle, and they killed almost all the train guards. You can't imagine how scared we were! I saw the Zapatistas on their horses with my own eyes, and I thought they were going to murder us all—or at least rob us. But I put myself in the hands of the Blessed Virgin, and she saved us."

A little worried by this information, I leaned out of my window trying to see something. Neither the locomotive nor any of the cars showed a single light. Whenever one of the passengers who had descended from the train struck a match to light a cigarette, the flame flared suddenly with a strange, enormous brilliance against the absolute blackness of the night.

Several hours went by—I don't know how many, for I had no watch and didn't ask anyone who had. Everything was quiet. The only sounds we heard were those of the tropical night. The train didn't move, and the passengers were growing restless. Each one was giving the others his theory as to the reasons for the delay. I, too, was beginning to be concerned. It was obvious that we would not reach Veracruz anywhere near the hour predicted in my instructions for finding my uncle, and I was frightened. But soon something else, of a more concrete and physiological nature, came along to take my mind off my apprehensions. "Those damned enchiladas!" I thought. "Or was it the pineapple? Well, I deserved it!" At first it was only a vague feeling of distress, but soon it became defined and localized as a stomachache. My misery came and went in painful spasms of the intestinal regions, accompanied by a cold sweat. It was getting worse. I had to find some way of relieving myself. I looked about me, trying to calculate the difficulties of getting through and over that world of sleeping human beings between my seat and the door marked Señores. We were a little less crowded now, for some of the people who had been standing in the aisle had got off the train and were walking up and down beside the coaches. The aisle was now occupied by women and children of all ages stretched out on the floor in deep slumber. My neighbor the merchant, too, was nodding. I hesitated, counting the number of steps I would have to take and trying to plan where to put my feet so as not to tread on any of the sleepers. But I didn't hesitate for long. A new cramp of Homeric proportions put an end to my qualms. I woke my neighbor to ask her to let me by and to watch my seat for a few minutes. I didn't have to explain my problem: it was written on my face, and perhaps evidenced by other phenomena.

"Don't be gone long," she said as she shifted her fat legs to let me pass. Hopping as carefully as I could over the recumbent bodies, I finally reached the door and eagerly turned the knob. It was locked from inside! I stood there for an eternal moment, until another spasm that doubled me up drove me to try the door again in the hope that it was merely jammed. I threw all my weight against it, but it didn't budge. I beat on the door with my fist.

"Just a minute!" someone called from inside, in a surly, sleepy voice. I couldn't wait any longer. I flew from the train, resolved

to satisfy my need in the open, anywhere I could. I could easily have done so only a few yards away in that utter darkness; but some inexplicable modesty made me wait until I was hidden in the brush some fifty paces from the coach. "Why didn't I think of this before?" I asked myself as I began to relieve the pressure of my intestines. The branches scratched and tickled, and suggested all kinds of creatures. Were there ants there? Or snakes? At last my torment was over. I was just starting to pull my clothes on when I heard the locomotive whistle, and the train immediately began to move. I could hardly make out the coaches, but I got my bearings from the headlight up ahead and from the sound of the wheels. I ran stumbling through the darkness and climbed aboard with some difficulty, for although the train was still moving slowly I couldn't see the steps. I had to make my way through a car clogged with people in order to reach mine. As I was fighting my way through the vestibule to the door, I saw a woman trying to persuade my seat companion to move over into my seat and give her hers. In my haste to get there in time to prevent this, I couldn't help stepping on a man stretched out on the floor.

"Look where you're going, stupid!" he cried. Paying no attention, I thanked the fat woman and slipped into my seat, panting.

"Where've you been? You almost lost your seat," she said.

"I almost got left behind!" I answered.

The train began to pick up speed. We had come to a section of track with a great many curves; the wheels grated with every turn and the timbers of the coach squeaked and groaned. On some of the tighter curves I could look out of my window and see the locomotive headlight coming toward us, as though it were trying to turn around and crash into the caboose. It was cold, and a light rain was falling. One by one all the windows were closed, except mine; I preferred the cold and even the rain to that smell of sleeping humanity. But soon people began to complain, and I had to shut it.

The lights had now been turned on, and in the yellow glow I watched the strange scene before me; it was like being inside a huge Red Cross ambulance filled with casualties. Almost all the passengers were asleep, some in the most unlikely positions. By peering through the people standing in the aisle I could see a terribly fat old man in the seat across from me; he was snoring open-mouthed, head back, and his stomach quivered with the motion of the train. A young man beside him—his son, probably —was nodding and falling against him from time to time. Another man in the typical costume of the tropical farmer was asleep on his feet leaning against the door, which he had blocked shut with some boxes. Whenever we braked or accelerated he seemed about to topple over; but by some miracle of the subconscious he would clutch the door, open his eyes, and manage to keep his balance. Soon he would be asleep again. A woman with a baby in her arms was huddled up near my seat, placidly snoring at the feet of a man dressed in black, who had the look of a provincial public employee. He was leaning freely against my seatmate, without apology; she accepted his weight with resignation, moving closer to me, and tried to sleep.

The monotonous click-clack of the rails seemed to be beating time for the chorus of snores, each one different, of that collective slumber, with its accompaniment of screeching wheels and crepitating framework.

The smell was unbearable. There was a stench of the barracks, of garbage, of unscoured toilets, in addition to that special, indescribable odor trains used to have: I don't know whether it was

fresh paint, or hot axle grease, or simply the accumulation of grime from all those trips.

Movement had always affected me, even as a small child. Swings always made me sick. Merry-go-rounds, Ferris wheels, and roller coasters were real torments for me. Naturally I got ill on streetcars, in automobiles, and especially on trains and boats. This sensitivity was now exaggerated by the penetrating smell and the stale air. The continual winding motion began to have its effect. My *lonche* and all the other things I had so rashly devoured began to cavort in my stomach. Although I wasn't sleepy, I began to yawn; then I noticed that my hands and face were sweating; my mouth filled with saliva; then came intermittent attacks of nausea, each one worse than the last. My head felt as if it were made of stone, and my legs turned to rubber. I had no will left, and I was sure that I wouldn't be able to move, even if I had to. But the fear of making a spectacle of myself by throwing up on my neighbor there in front of everybody overcame my lassitude; I waited for a moment when I felt relatively well, stood up, and without a word pushed my way past the fat lady and headed for the toilet as fast as I could go. The door marked Señores was still locked. I beat on it furiously, first with my fists and then with my feet.

"What a nuisance!" The voice from within was the same that had called out, "Just a minute!" an hour earlier. Just then my stomach contracted uncontrollably and my mouth filled with a horribly bitter liquid. Keeping my mouth closed by a superhuman effort, I threw myself against the door. I felt the contents of my stomach rising in my throat and flooding into my nose, hot and disgusting. Unable to reply to the eternal occupant, I went on kicking the door; but it didn't open. At last I spat out that mouthful made up of God only knows what ingredients, put my mouth to the keyhole, and called, "Please open up! Please!" The door flew open almost at once, and the angry occupant—whom I had noticed earlier trying to find a seat—let me in.

"A man has to sit some place," he said, as if that explained everything.

The latrine smell in that dirty little windowless room and the look of the black hole beneath which you could picture the railroad ties going by brought on a new attack of nausea. Clutching the water supply pipe with both hands, I leaned over and vomited like a poisoned dog. With the swaying of the train my spew fell everywhere: it spattered the floor, the seat, the bowl, the walls, my shoes. At last my stomach was completely empty, and the contractions produced nothing more than hiccups.

I don't know how long I was in that torture chamber. Sweating but feeling much better, I turned to wash my face in the little battered tin washbowl fastened to the wall opposite the toilet. There was no water, unfortunately. I wiped my perspiring face with my handkerchief and headed back to my seat, but I was disagreeably surprised to find it occupied by the lady who had been sleeping on the floor with her baby. I was too weak to fight for what I believed to be my rights; besides, I couldn't bring myself to argue the matter with a woman in her circumstances. I stood leaning against the wall next to the farmer, who was still asleep on his feet by the door, and rejoiced in my new-found health. I prepared to spend the rest of the journey in a vertical position. The former occupant of the rest room had seen me emerge and quickly ran back in. I couldn't help smiling at the surprise that awaited him. He certainly wouldn't be able to sleep on the toilet as peacefully as he had before.

We reached Veracruz at three in the morning. It was pouring. In all my life I have never seen rain like that. The water fell, not in drops, but in a veritable curtain, a cascade. The streetcars had stopped running, of course, and there was no other transportation. What to do? It didn't even cross my mind to take a hotel room for the rest of the night; I had no idea how much it would cost, but I was sure that the few pesos I had left in my pocket would not be enough. I considered the possibility of sitting in the station until dawn, but then I remembered that I wouldn't be able to find my uncle in the daytime, for the theater would be closed. My only hope was that there might be a light on in his house: no one but an actor would be up at that hour. Since the theater, where I was to ask for him, would not be open, and my other directions were so vague, I had only one chance of success. He might have gone out for supper after the theater, and might be coming home at this hour. Following this line of reasoning, I plunged out into the street in spite of the rain.

I asked several people to direct me to the Eslava Theater. They stared at me incredulously. What the devil did I want at the theater this time of night? At last a policeman who had taken shelter under the roof of an abandoned fruit stand listened to my story; he told me that the shortest way would be to turn left and follow the streetcar line. I would be there in about half an hour.

I followed his directions. The rain, which stopped occasionally and then came down again in a fury, was not unpleasant. I had never felt rain as warm as this; in Mexico City it was always cold. Besides, it was such a hot night that a bath felt rather good. My black hat had wilted, and did little more than keep the rain out of my eyes; the water poured off it in torrents down my back. I hurried along the streetcar tracks, plunging heedlessly through the puddles. At times the water barely covered my shoes, but occasionally it was up to my knees. My stockings were glued to my flesh. But in my eagerness to reach the theater none of this mattered.

From time to time I worried a little about the clothes in my suitcase, for it was made of wicker and the water went right through
it.

I stopped only once. That was in front of a grocery store, where
several Spaniards were laughingly engaged in hunting down some
enormous rats. They were slaughtering them with clubs and kicks,
amid cries of rather doubtful propriety, and it looked like fun; but
I had no time to lose, and went on my way.

Finally the marquee of the theater came into sight. Since the
lights were out, I had some difficulty reading the name. When I
saw that it was the Eslava, and that it was deserted, I went around
the block to the street behind it, sure that I would see a light in
my uncle's house.

The street was in total darkness. Every door and window on
both sides was closed, and not a glimmer of light showed through
any crack. I found a pile of sand and gravel in the gutter and
climbed up on it to get out of the water and look around. Suddenly a light came on in one of the windows. I went straight to it,
sure that I had found the house. Before knocking, I peered
through the door; like many doors in the tropics, it was made of
wooden slats, and you could see inside. There was a man squat-
ting on the floor with his back to me, dressed only in shorts; he
looked to me like a Chinaman. I knocked. He got up and came
to the door, but I still couldn't make out his face.

"Who is it?"

"It's me," I answered stupidly.

The door swung open and a familiar face appeared before me.
It was not my Uncle Manuel but his brother Arturo, who I didn't
know was in Veracruz. He stared at me, unable to believe his eyes.

"What in the world are you doing here, my boy?" he asked
with a smile. When I had explained that Alfonso had sent me to

stay with Manuel, he sat down on a canvas cot and began to laugh heartily.

"Stay with Manuel!" he chuckled. "Kid, don't you know your Uncle Manuel left for Havana three days ago? But come in, come in and shut the door," he added, since I was still standing there.

I was dumbfounded. I took off my dripping coat and hung it on a chair, and then I opened my suitcase. What I saw there was horrible. Everything was wet, and bright red. *Marianela,* its lovely red binding now limp, had stained all my clothes.

I undressed and went to bed on a canvas cot that stood next to my uncle's; soon after I had pulled the unbleached muslin sheet over me I fell fast asleep.

Thus began my two months' stay in Veracruz, where I was to spend an unforgettable vacation with that uncle fate had unexpectedly provided. The friendship that sprang up between us was unusual for two persons of such different ages. He was the editor of the newspaper *El Pueblo.* The delightful conversations we had during our long early-morning walks home from his office, about the meaning of the Revolution and the future of our country, were to have a decisive influence on my thinking, both as a youth and as a grown man.

San Vicente Chicoloapan

My brother arrived unexpectedly one Saturday morning. He was accompanied by my cousin Darío and two friends; all of them were very young and had just joined Carranza's army. They had come to invite me to spend a few days of my brief school vacation with them in San Vicente Chicoloapan, a village near Mexico City, where they were stationed. I was delighted. Going to the front appealed to me immensely, because everyone there rode horseback; that alone was enough to compensate for any inconvenience, discomfort, or danger there might be. My brother wore the campaign uniform of the time, and proudly displayed on his

Stetson a gold bar denoting his rank as second lieutenant. At eighteen he was slender, with very white skin and blond, curly hair, and looked more like a student from a military prep school than a real soldier or an authentic revolutionary. Nevertheless, he took his rank very seriously—as he did his entire army career—and nothing would have offended him as much as hearing me make such an observation. Faithful to his role as older brother, he hastened to point out the hardships and annoyances that I would have to put up with in camp. I would have to live like the rest of them: sleeping on the ground; getting up at reveille; eating whatever I could get—usually little more than a piece of fried meat and some tortillas with chile, or perhaps some beans; drinking pulque, because water was scarce and unsafe; and suffering heat and cold. In short, I would have to lead the life of a soldier on campaign. Then too, although things were pretty quiet at the moment, it was not impossible that the Zapatistas might move up or that our side might be ordered to advance or even engage them in battle. If that should happen, the danger would be very real, and he was warning me in advance to stay out of it. It all sounded fine to me, and the hazards merely added a romantic flavor. It would be an unusual experience for a boy of my age, even in those times.

Besides, anything would be better than my present loneliness. I was happy to know that for a few days I wouldn't have to get up in the morning and fetch the milk from the neighboring dairy, get bread at the corner store—begging for credit at both places—and eat breakfast all by myself. Not to mention the fact that the excursion would give me an excellent excuse for not sweeping the house the following Sunday—the day I dedicated to housecleaning—and especially for not dusting under the beds, where that unique kind of lint grew so inexorably. This was a fuzz inhabited by millions of fleas who, as soon as they were disturbed by the broom, sprang out in all directions and covered my stockings in a brown sheath.

I hastily put on a well-worn pair of riding pants and an old wool shirt of my brother's, and strapped on a pair of his leggings; the leather was not the same color as my shoes, but they made it look a little as though I were wearing riding boots. I felt grown up; a revolutionary who needed only a pistol and a pair of cartridge belts to strike fear into the beholder.

We left the city that morning from the San Lázaro station, on the freight and passenger train that went as far as Texcoco. We bought no tickets; we simply boarded the last coach. No one seemed surprised to see us, and no one came to collect our fares. People probably thought we were part of the train's armed escort. Perhaps it would turn out that we were!

The train moved slowly, with long stops not only at stations but, inexplicably, in the open country. At this rate it took us four hours to cover the few miles between Mexico City and San Vicente Chicoloapan. We jumped off as soon as we saw the little station with its sign that read San Vicente. The railroads used only the Christian part of village names; thus they ignored a tradition established by the conquistadors, who always juxtaposed the Spanish and Indian designations—a custom that exemplifies the mingling of races in Mexico, obvious even in the naming of many towns.

Near the station, which was the only building in sight, a couple of soldiers were waiting for us with five horses. The animals reared as the little, noisy locomotive struggled laboriously to get the train under way again. I counted the horses, and saw that there wasn't one for me; including the two soldiers, there were six of us. My brother, seeing the disappointment on my face, explained that we would get one for me at headquarters. In the meantime I would have to ride with him.

We covered the short distance from the station to the village at full gallop. We raised a hellish dust and filled the air with jubilant whoops that were intended to sound warlike, but actually were not much different from those of so many children playing cops and robbers. We thought we were being funny, but the sentries took our simulated enemy attack for the real thing. Thus when we reached the main gate we were met by a small detachment of guards with rifles at the ready, accompanied by the corps commander himself. He did not find our noisy raid at all amusing. He was introduced to me as Lieutenant Colonel Berástegui; later I learned that his officers called him "Bizcuástegui," because of his severely crossed eyes.* I soon saw that he was a man who took himself very seriously, and was eager to ingratiate himself with the general in command of the brigade. He was not at all like the other officers, most of whom were extremely young and consequently short on dignity and long on high spirits. Bizcuástegui shook my hand and, without looking at anyone in particular so as to conceal his squint, observed, "Another snot-nosed kid!" Then he turned on his heel and went back into his office.

That afternoon I had a marvelous time. We went for a long ride that was called a "reconnaissance," but for me it was simply an enjoyable outing. I was riding a small, spirited, young chestnut, wore a full cartridge belt across my chest, and carried a 30-30 on the right side of my saddle. I felt happy and important and ready for any adventure, heedless of the discomfort of that armament to which I was unaccustomed and which I hardly knew how to use. The rifle made a bulge on the right side of the saddle tree, so that my stirrups were uneven; and the cartridge belt kept banging me in the chest and back whenever I trotted or galloped. But what

* From *bizco,* cross-eyed. *Tr.*

were these annoyances compared with the joy of racing across the countryside or simply riding at a walk beside my brother, drinking in the sunshine on the Mexican Plateau?

Night was falling when we returned to camp, weary and covered with dust. We hadn't eaten all day, and I was as hungry as a wolf. When I smelled the pork frying in a great copper pan outside the barracks and the coffee boiling in its pot, and heard the sound of women slapping tortillas, I grew even more ravenous. I wished I could have had a bath, but there was barely enough water to wash our hands and splash our faces.

Supper was delicious and the company agreeable. There was a lot of joking about "domestic hunting," for it had been necessary to shoot a small pig in the yard of one of the neighboring houses. I felt sorry for the unlucky villager who hadn't been able to get it out of sight quickly enough; but that didn't keep me from enjoying my supper. I could see that we had to get provisions some way. The fortunes of war!

I slept badly that night. The ground was hard, and I couldn't get warm under my thin blanket. Besides, it was uncomfortable sleeping in my trousers. At night we removed only our shoes and shirt, in case of an enemy attack and because no one even dreamed of carrying more clothing than what he had on his back. I suffered all night, too, from a horrible itching. I didn't know what caused it until the next morning, when I was revolted to see and smell a veritable army of bedbugs on my neighbor's blanket. There were so many of them that the sarape itself seemed to be moving.

We got up at the sound of reveille. A splash of cool water on my face and a cup of watery coffee with a typical sweet roll from the village restored my good humor, which had been considerably damaged by a bad night and by my being roused out of bed so early. I was fascinated by the preparations going on about me: the

seemingly disorganized milling about, the cursing whenever one of the horses refused the bit, the issuing of orders by the officers. As soon as I possibly could I began saddling the stocky little horse I had ridden the day before. My eagerness was not shared by the others, who knew what kind of an expedition we were in for. My brother didn't seem very cheerful, and I could see that he was worried. "It would be better if you didn't come along," he told me. "This maneuver could be dangerous, and there's no reason for you to risk getting yourself shot. If I let anything happen to you, I'd never forgive myself." He added, after a moment, "I shouldn't have brought you here."

For a while it looked as if my trip to San Vicente Chicoloapan was turning out to be a total failure, and I felt humiliated. I can't say that the prospect of danger—about which I had only the vaguest of notions—appealed to me; but I panicked at the thought of being left behind with the baggage, with no brother to keep me company and tell me what to do. I must persuade him to take me with him. I pointed out that it might also be unsafe to remain in an undefended village: the Zapatistas could very easily attack, for it would be evident that our troops had left.

I don't think this argument really convinced my brother, but he finally agreed to let me come along. Perhaps he did so for the same reason that I had not been able to bring myself to express: I would be ashamed if the others thought I was afraid. I couldn't stay behind with the women; I had to take my chances with the men.

We left the village in an orderly fashion, although not in any regular military formation that I could see. We moved along in small groups, a few yards apart. Nobody talked, and the only sound was that of the horses' hoofs on the hard dirt road. The morning was cool and clear, with a blue sky in which a few small white clouds scudded before a wind of which there was no indication whatsoever below. We took deep breaths of that thin, pure atmosphere the Europeans call "mountain air"—although the terrain was flat except for little hills covered with maguey and dotted with pepper trees. It was the typical landscape of the Mexican Central Plateau, rather bleak but not without a certain poetic charm. The cactus on both sides of the road and the maguey plants that stretched out in parallel rows as far as the eye could see were covered with an ashy film of dust that had settled there since the last rain, several weeks before.

When we reached a dry river bed we came to a halt. By this time it was beginning to get hot. Lieutenant Colonel Bizcuástegui called his officers together for their orders. They gathered in a little group under a pepper tree, whose red berries stood out vividly against the pale green foliage, rather dusty now. He took only a few minutes to give them the plan of action, which my brother later explained briefly. We were to take a small Zapatista village a few miles ahead. Our detachment, consisting of about thirty men, was to advance along the river bed, while the bulk of our forces would spread out to the right in an encircling movement and approach the village from behind. We were not to fire unless fired upon, or until we heard that the attack had begun.

We went up the river bed—which looked as if there had never been any water in it—in single file, trying to keep to the right under the protection of the bank. We had orders to keep silent and move slowly to avoid raising dust. I could see the main body— some hundred and fifty men—off to the right, moving along a dry ditch that must at one time have been an irrigation canal, where they could not be seen from the town.

Although the rest were older than I, we were nearly all youngsters, and it was hard to pretend that we weren't nervous. No one said a word, and every face was a little pale. We had readied our rifles and were carrying them in our right hand, with the reins in our left. I was behind my brother, and behind me was one of his grammar school friends, a boy named Luna. Almost all of the group were friends who had enlisted at the same time—a little in the spirit of adventure, a little because of revolutionary indoctrination, and mostly because the unrest of the times made it impossible for them either to finish their education or to find a job. These young men, with or without commissions—there was not much formality in these matters at the time—made up the officers' corps. The rest of the army had been recruited from the slums of Mexico City in the past few months. Almost all of them were absolute rookies, although two officers and a few of the men had taken part in the northern campaign; these, who had had more experience in such matters, considered themselves, and were, real veterans compared to us. They regarded us with scorn, and did their best to make a show of valor that they, too, perhaps did not really feel.

We advanced slowly, trying not to be seen or heard, our heads brushing against the bushes on the bank at our right. Our horses were nose to tail. An invisible cloud of apprehension was beginning to settle over us. Our mounts moved carefully and rhythmically, with a sound like running water; occasionally the monotony was broken when one of the horses stumbled on a boulder. My little chestnut, Airplane, had fortunately forgotten his former high spirits and was walking with his head down, only rolling his bit from time to time. Several times he broke the silence with a sneeze, which in our fear of being discovered seemed deafening.

The lead rider stopped, and we did the same. We could hear something in the distance, but we couldn't tell whether it was voices, the sound of horses' hoofs, or merely the wind soughing in the trees. Soon we heard a few rifle shots off to the right, then more, and then others farther away and more widely spaced—as though whoever was shooting were taking careful aim. At the same time we noticed a sound like bees buzzing over our heads. We were ordered to dismount and stand by our horses. The shots were getting closer and more deliberate, and each one was doubled by its echo from the hills. When they finally stopped, I gave Luna my reins and cautiously climbed up the parapet made by the river bank, on my stomach, to see what was going on. By peering through the grass and brush I could see the town, which was quite close. There was one little house standing by itself on the outskirts, like a lookout; the village began some three hundred yards beyond it. Everything was quiet. I crawled a little higher, still hidden by the brush, and was able to make out some tiny figures moving on the other side of the town. I could see that they were on horseback, but I couldn't tell whether they were ours or the enemy. Suddenly I was terrified to hear the sound of galloping horses, quite near. I slid back down the bank and waited there with the others, hardly daring to breathe. At last one of the veteran officers, who had also climbed the bank, turned and announced, "They're our men! They're going into the village!"

With that he leaped on his sorrel and took off at a trot over the loose gravel of the river bed, scattering pebbles in all directions. We quickly mounted and went on, first at a walk and then at a trot, until we came to a place where the arroyo widened and the bank was less steep. We shot out at a gallop. As we picked up speed we grew more excited, and some of us began firing our rifles in the air and letting out jubilant whoops.

We rode into the poor little hamlet by way of a dusty road that ran between two rows of ancient cactuses. There was a growing cloud of dust over the rooftops, announcing that our comrades had preceded us. It was a typical small Indian town, with one-storied adobe houses along a main street that was intersected by four or five others at right angles. The squat, identical houses were in wretched condition. Some of the walls facing the street had once been whitewashed but were now peeling from the effects of sun and rain; most of them, however, displayed the muddy color of untreated adobe. The village seemed to be clutching the foot of the hill, and was surrounded on all sides by green maguey fields; the monotony was relieved only by an occasional yellow patch where corn had been planted. The cornfields were completely dried up now.

Just as we arrived, Lieutenant Colonel Berástegui and his men rode in at an easy gallop from the opposite side of town.

"The sons-of-bitches got away from us," he observed, as though to himself. Then, indicating with a gesture that some of us were to follow him, he said, "Let's see what we can find."

We rode up to the nearest house. Without dismounting he pounded on the door with the butt of his rifle—a small weapon of a make I'd never seen before. The door swung open. He called out, "Come on out of there!"

There was no answer. After a moment we got off our horses.

"Come out, damn you!" Bizcuástegui called again. His words were swallowed up in the darkness inside the miserable hut. "Looks like nobody's here," he said. "Let's take a look."

He started to ride in, but his horse stumbled on the doorsill and reared; he dismounted and entered the murky room, pistol in hand. We followed close behind with our rifles at the ready. There was no one there. After the heat and the dust outside, this house with its strong odor of wood smoke felt pleasantly damp and cool. When our eyes grew accustomed to the darkness we could see that we were in a typical Indian home: a single cubicle that served as living room, bedroom, dining room, and kitchen.

There was no furniture, properly speaking, except for an old wobbly wooden chair with a rush bottom. On the floor at our left, coals were still glowing under a thick earthenware griddle, on which smoked the remains of some corn tortillas, now burned and dry. Near the hearth stood a rectangular stone mortar containing half-ground tortilla dough, and beside it a gourd bowl filled with corn. On the other side of the mortar was a flat basket heaped with the thick tortillas called *gordas,* lovingly covered with a white cotton napkin embroidered in red. An earthenware pot of beans was still boiling on the three stones of another cooking fire nearby. Leaning against the wall near the door stood a rolled-up grass mat, looking like a person who hoped no one would notice him. In the farthest corner, on our right, we could barely make out (there was no light but that which came in through the door, and the Colonel's horse was blocking some of that) a wooden box lined with rags that was undoubtedly an infant's cradle. The smoke in the room burned our eyes and made it hard to breathe; it floated along the walls and ceiling and billowed out the door. That day I understood why our indigenous people smell of wood smoke.

What I saw there gave me an odd feeling, a mixture of sadness and apprehension. It was obvious that the village had been abandoned in great haste a few minutes before our arrival. I reflected uneasily that they surely couldn't be very far away; we might be attacked from behind at any moment. And yet at the same time it was equally obvious that the inhabitants were peaceful country people—as witnessed the order and tranquility in that cool, dark room—who had taken flight from their modest homes at our approach. The men who searched the other houses found very much the same thing. If it had not been for these evidences of daily routine to be found everywhere, the town would have seemed uninhabited. Only in the village store did we come across a living being: one of those mangy, emaciated dogs of no known breed. The store was merely an ordinary house like the others, but had once been painted blue; over the door, in black letters, was the name of the establishment: THE AURORA. The poor dog came out of a corner of the small vestibule with his tail between his legs, growling and showing his yellow, ruined teeth, as though he meant to defend someone inside. We were sure that at last we were going to find a human being; we searched the place cautiously, but found no one.

Bizcuástegui was visibly annoyed. His coup had failed. Those damned "sneaky" Indians must be hiding in the maguey; but we weren't to go looking for them, for we would be exposing ourselves to a shotgun blast in the face, without ever knowing where it came from.

We mounted again and headed back to camp. I felt depressed and sort of empty inside, as though I had done something wrong. I felt that we had violated something sacred, that we had committed an unforgivable offense, an unjustifiable and pointless outrage. Most of the others were in a talkative mood, eager to discuss the part they had played in the unsuccessful attack and filled with euphoria now that the tension was over. But I couldn't share their high spirits.

About halfway back to camp we saw two people on the road ahead of us. As is the custom in Mexico, the woman was perched on the rump of a burro and the man was walking behind. As they were going in the same direction we were, and as there were no other settlements nearby, it was logical to assume that they had come from the village we had just left. The Colonel ordered two of the men to ride ahead and stop them. This they quickly did, and a few minutes later we were gathered around the couple. The man, dressed in the typical white cotton shirt and trousers, looked to be about thirty; although his almost beardless face was so wrinkled by the sun and weather that he could easily have been older. The woman was much younger and seemed quite good-looking—it was hard to tell, for her shawl covered most of her face and her body was hidden under a voluminous skirt.

Several of the officers began interrogating them in a desultory way, but could get nothing out of them. The peasant and his wife merely kept repeating, "We're peaceful citizens, Little Masters. We're little peaceful people." Bizcuástegui put an end to the confusion by ordering his men to tie the husband's hands and bring him along at the end of a rope fastened to one of their saddle horns. He told the woman she could go on her way if she liked. She refused, and seeing who was in charge, began to plead with the Colonel in a piteous voice.

"Please, Little Master, don't hurt my man. In the name of the Blessed Virgin, for the sake of his little children, Señor Master."

The Colonel answered that he had no quarrel with her, but that her husband was a Zapatista, and must be taken to headquarters for questioning. If she wanted to come along, she could.

We went on again, less gaily than before. The man trotted along at the end of his rope, stumbling from time to time. The woman, still muffled in her dark green shawl, followed on the burro, beating it on the neck and haunches with a twig from a quince tree. They didn't speak, or even look at each other. I couldn't possibly have guessed what was going on in their minds; they were as much Mexicans as I was, and yet they seemed far removed from me and from the time we lived in. They were like foreigners from a distant and exotic land.

When we got to camp the Colonel ordered the prisoner brought into his office for questioning. The man stood impassively before him with lowered eyes, straw hat in hand; on his bowed head his thick, straight hair grew in its natural directions, like that of some preclassical Greek statues I was to see many years later. His coarse, dirty feet were shod in battered huaraches. One of them was bleeding; a blackish paste of blood and dust oozed from between his toes and ran slowly onto the floor, leaving a red stain. I suppose one of the horses had stepped on him, or he had cut it on a sharp stone in the road. The Indian took no notice. He twisted his hat in his hands and waited patiently.

"Where did the people from your village go?" Bizcuástegui demanded.

"I don't know, Little Master."

"You're a Zapatista. Isn't that right?"

"No, Señor Master."

"If you don't tell me the truth, we're going to give you a *cintareada*. Do you understand?"

The Indian's face was expressionless.

"Do you know what a *cintareada* is?"

"No, Little Master."

The Colonel asked someone to bring him an old sword he had in his office. He took it from its scabbard and held it up in front of the Indian.

"A *cintareada* is a sword-whipping, a good beating with the flat of this sword. Would you like that?"

"No, Señor Master."

"Then tell me where everybody went when they left the village."

The man seemed not to hear him. Bizcuástegui spoke slowly, making an effort to keep calm.

"All right, then at least tell me who tipped you off."

"I don't know anything, Señor Master. That's God's truth. You can beat me if you want to."

After the failure of his punitive expedition, the Colonel had to vent his fury in some way. He handed the sword to one of the soldiers and said, "Give him three strokes."

The sword whistled through the air and bent twice across the poor man's back and once across his buttocks. There was no cry of pain, nor any change of expression in the Indian's face. Only a slight contraction of his facial muscles betrayed that he was clenching his teeth. There was a horrible silence. My heart was pounding, as though I were the one who was being beaten. I had never before seen anyone strike a defenseless adult human being. Besides, a basic sense of justice within me was outraged by such punishment inflicted on a man who could very easily have been innocent.

"Where did those damned Indians go?"

Bizcuástegui was shouting furiously by this time.

The Indian didn't deign to answer. He didn't even look up.

"Let him have another ten," the Colonel said, his face flushed with anger.

The sword whistled again.

I couldn't stand it. I left the room, feeling sick.

When I came out into the yard, I saw by brother sitting on a stone that had once been part of a bench built against the wall. He beckoned me, and when I reached his side I demanded an explanation. I asked what the man could be guilty of. If he was a Zapatista, why wasn't he dealt with in the proper way? If, as he claimed, he was just a peaceful citizen, why was he being so brutally mistreated? Nothing in my experience had prepared me to understand this kind of fury, or to make a guess as to the tortuous currents in the Colonel's soul.

"Don't watch things like that," he told me. "They're horrible and stupid. The least hateful thing about war is the fighting. The worst part of it are these scenes of unnecessary cruelty."

How far he was still from adapting himself to the life of barracks and campaigns, a life to which he would eventually become so inured! He was still the prep school student, blond and neat, under that layer of dust that covered his face and uniform, whitening his eyebrows and lashes until he looked like an albino.

We sat there without speaking for several minutes, until he got up and left when a soldier brought him some order or other. I headed for the main gate, intending to take a walk out in the country; but I met David coming from the direction of the railway station. He was the son of the caretaker at my grandmother's house, and bore the nickname "Handy"—because, to use our childish expression, he was "very handy with his fists." He had enlisted at the same time as our friends and relatives; although he was only a private, he seemed more pleased with his lot than any of us. He was delighted with this new life, free from the restrictions of the city and civilization. He had been running, and was breathing hard. He winked and said:

"I hear they brought us a good-looking dame. Boy, have I been needing something like that!"

At once the young Indian woman came to my mind. Could it be possible?

That's who it was, all right. The poor man hadn't uttered another word in spite of his sword-whipping, and Bizcuástegui had had to let him go; but to punish him for his obstinacy he had let the men take his wife to the barn—or, as the soldiers said, laugh-

ing, "put her up before the firing squad." I couldn't resist the
temptation of going to see what was happening. I felt both curiosity and dread: attraction and repugnance. I walked toward the
barn, trying to look nonchalant. It was a huge rectangular structure of stone, like a fortress, that had served as a storehouse for the
old hacienda. There were a dozen soldiers standing in line in the
doorway; they were whispering among themselves, but when I
came up they stopped. Handy, who was there waiting his turn,
said to me, "Not you; you're not old enough. This woman is very
hot-blooded, and if you get into her you'll get a disease."

I couldn't think of anything to say. I had no intention of taking
part in something that so repelled and frightened me; I was convinced that I had come only to satisfy a certain uneasy curiosity.
But I didn't dare tell him that, especially in front of the others. I
was sure they would laugh at me for a prig, or, worse yet from an
adolescent's point of view, would guess that I was totally inex-
perienced. My first impulse was to walk away, but my pride and
an unhealthy fascination kept me there. Without a word I went
past the line of soldiers and entered the barn.

There was a little light coming in through a half-open window,
but until my eyes adjusted themselves to the darkness I couldn't
make out anything very clearly. At one end there were some bales
of alfalfa, and near it a mound of loose straw, on which I could
see two human bodies moving rhythmically. I wanted to go closer,
but I was afraid. My mouth felt dry, my hands were sweating, and
my legs began to tremble. I leaned against the wall. Suddenly the
man got to his feet, and I could see the woman who had been lying
beneath him. A beam of sunlight fell on one dun thigh, amid
rumpled clothing and wisps of straw. The man turned and headed
for the door, fastening his belt; as he passed me I saw an expres-

sion on his face that was half shame and half satisfaction. The woman hastened to cover herself with her skirt.

The leader of the group, whom the others called "Sarge," called out, "Who's next?"

A tall, skinny boy stepped forward at once, but Sarge stopped him.

"Not yet, Snipe. You've got the clap, and we've got to keep you isolated. Back to the end of the line!"

The boy obeyed, grumbling. I stood against the wall near the door and watched as twelve men, one after another, satisfied their lust. There was no gaiety, no air of festivity, and, of course, neither tenderness nor affection. It was more like a kind of ceremony. As soon as each one finished he stood up, turned his back on the woman, rearranged his clothing, and walked away, fastening his belt. Each time the woman instinctively covered her legs. Then another soldier approached, and the scene was repeated. At last Snipe's turn came. I had been watching him. He was small and very dark, with a short nose and a wide, laughing mouth. He had been a shoeshine boy in Mexico City, and owed his nickname to the fact that he was terribly skinny and had a peculiar way of walking that was reminiscent of a bird. His gait was the result of an inflammation of the inguinal glands—or of his "buboes," as he proudly announced. We all knew he had a particularly virulent form of gonorrhea; he boasted of it, for he thought it proved his virility.

Everyone had gone but Sarge, Snipe, and myself. I went up to Sarge.

"Please, Sarge, don't let him! You know he's got a terrible disease. The poor woman!"

Sarge gave me a knowing smile; perhaps he was thinking that

my advice was not totally disinterested. Then he said, "You're right, kid. Get out of here, Snipe! Don't be such a pig!"

While the boy was demanding his rights, the woman took advantage of the lull to get up and make her way slowly to the door. When I saw that she was leaving I felt strangely disconsolate. Perhaps at the back of my mind there had been more than curiosity when I decided to visit the barn. But it was too late now. Sarge kept watching me out of the corner of his eye, while I, in turn, couldn't take my eyes off the Indian woman. I knew now that I desired her. To me she seemed beautiful in her attitude of resignation, and admirable in her dignity. She had not uttered a single word of complaint; she had never once tried to defend herself; she had hurled no insults at the men who had violated her. She had submitted to that unjustifiable assault with an oriental fatalism. I had the feeling that she was detached from what was happening to her; it was not that she was indifferent, but that she was aware of her own dignity, and confident that in spite of this barbaric outrage her honor as a woman and as a wife had remained untouched. As she passed by us she threw a rapid glance in our direction, and I saw in her eyes the look of a wounded and cornered animal. Her black pupils glistened with hatred and lust for vengeance. It was only for an instant; then she lowered her head and left the barn soundlessly, seeming to glide over the ground on her bare feet. She crossed the yard, went through the gate, and disappeared.

A few days later I had to return to Azcapotzalco and everyday things: classes at the Preparatory, long trips in the second class streetcar, the unbearable loneliness. But I couldn't forget that woman's eyes with their inner fire, their glint of hatred, nor the sorrow and the shame. I couldn't study. The scene in the barn kept coming back to project itself on the pages of mathematical formulas and the illustrations in my botany text. And always there was the same question: how could the revolutionaries, of whom my father had spoken so enthusiastically, and who, according to my last teacher in primary school, had taken up arms to defend the common people and especially the indigenous races, commit outrages like this? At my age and with the little experience I had, I was unable to distinguish between the underlying motives of a social movement such as the one Mexico went through from 1910 on and the sometimes shameful incidents that occurred during its career because of the needs, the vices, and the cruelty of men. And although I didn't admit it to myself, there was another question to be answered: had I myself not been on the point of joining those barbarians?

The Bull

He was dark-haired and gangling, with the pale skin of those who come from our coastal malarial regions; but to judge from his accent he was not a Mexican. It was hard to tell where he was from. He lisped *c* and *z* like a Spaniard, but some of his expressions were typically Cuban; there was a certain trace, too, of an American accent. Although he was obviously a shy boy, we soon fell into conversation. With the frankness and familiarity of boys of our age, the first thing I asked was why he talked in such a funny way. My question didn't seem to annoy him, although he did appear a little embarrassed, as though his accent were something to be ashamed of. He explained the matter in the systematic manner of a professor expounding a complex subject. And yet his way of speaking was oddly unpedantic, perhaps because of his sorrowful face and soft voice—characteristics I was later to know so well.

He had been born in Mexico of Spanish parents. His father and mother were both painters, and had been traveling all over the world almost continually from the time he was an infant. They had lived in Spain, in Cuba, and most recently in California, where he had had most of his primary schooling. The constant changing of schools, of surroundings, and above all of languages had been a hindrance in his studies and had troubled him a great deal. Just when he had adapted himself to a milieu he would have to move to another country, enroll in another school, often after the year had already begun, and make new friends. Because of this he had developed a talent for mimicry: he unconsciously took on the accent of the region where he happened to be living. In Tampico, for example, he had acquired the habit of dropping his *s*'s. He had picked up his tropical intonation in Havana. His Madrid-born mother had given him the double *l* (which was so noticeable when he said *cabal-yo*) and the lisped *z* of his *thapatos*. His father was an Andalusian, and, like his son, aspirated the *h*, saying *jace* instead of *hace*. This last the boy denied indignantly.

His clothing was as remarkable as his accent. At fifteen he still wore short pants in the European fashion, and his long, skinny legs were conspicuous in any group of Preparatory students at the ancient colonial building on San Ildefonso (where we were now attending classes after a year in the Doghouse). We would have thought it an intolerable disgrace not to be allowed to wear long pants, and so did he; but he hadn't been able to convince his parents of this. They insisted that he dress "properly," no matter what his friends wore. In the United States this had been a real martyrdom, he said, for American children had a veritable cult of uniformity and standarization; there was no one they had greater contempt for than the boy who tried to be different, individual, or extraordinary either in dress, thought, or speech. When I knew him better I came to realize that this American characteristic had left its mark on him: he always aspired to be a member of the group, to "belong," as he said (literally translating the English word by *pertenecer*). The most extraordinary thing about this ambition was that he had never realized it, and never would. There were several reasons for this, but it was principally because he was really and truly an exceptional human being who could not hope to pass unnoticed.

Thanks to my intervention with his parents, he was finally allowed to don long trousers and dress like the rest of us; and by constant effort he began to lose his idiosyncrasies of intonation and accent. But he was still different from the other boys, and, since he never overcame his shyness, was deeply disturbed by the fact.

Incredibly enough, in spite of his natural timidity he couldn't resist being an outstanding student. It was always he who knew the lesson, who raised his hand at every question, who punctually turned in his homework correctly done, with no mistakes and so neatly written that it could not possibly be confused with anyone else's.

Two ambitions were engaged in a bitter struggle within him: one was to be like everybody else, while the other was to be the most distinguished. Whenever he recited in class there was an embarrassed note in his voice, as though he were begging his schoolmates to forgive him; his huge brown eyes took on a humble expression that seemed to say, in that faintly Spanish accent, "Don't hold it against me. I'm perfectly aware that all of you know the lesson as well as I do; but we have to keep the teacher happy."

This inner conflict was evident in sports, too. I saw this for the first time at the Young Men's Christian Association. It was there that he acquired his nickname: "The Bull."

It was my first visit to the Y.M.C.A. Everything was strange: the turnstile that could be opened by remote control by the dressing room custodian; the little wire baskets in which they issued our newly washed and ironed uniforms—the white shorts, the T-shirt, the tennis shoes, the woolen socks, all stained but clean, washed by machine; the special smell of the shower rooms, made up of soap, talcum powder, and sweat; the gym with its varnished floor, its circular race track on the upper level, and its numerous pieces of apparatus for all kinds of physical exercise; the easy comradery of the boys and the studied seriousness of the "leaders." (We used the English word.)

When we entered the gym together that morning, a few of the members were standing about chatting as they waited for the calisthenics class to begin. Someone called out, "Yeah! Here comes the Bull!" I turned around to see who they meant, and saw an innocent, childlike smile on my friend's face. There could be no doubt.

"Why do they call you the Bull?" I asked.

"No reason. Just to say something stupid," he said in an embarrassed way.

"Red" Ochoa directed the class, with a great show of magnificent muscles and a lot of jokes; the latter seemed rather forced, and a little imitative of American humor. When the class was over the older boys left, and we remained to play basketball. Before the game had even begun, my friend snatched the ball from the

Rooster (a dark-haired youth with a black mustache waxed to needle points, who was an excellent player and all-around athlete), dribbled the entire length of the court, bowling over everyone in his path, and tried unsuccessfully for a basket. There was no longer any need to explain why they called him the Bull. He really looked like one as he charged straight ahead, heedless of all obstacles, head down, bouncing the ball with his right hand and warding off his adversaries with his left. He was a veritable fighting bull who had just dashed into the arena, dazzled by the sudden sunlight, charging—though ineffectively—anything that moved.

To be quite accurate, he moved more like a Great Dane than a bull. Like a puppy of that breed, his feet and hands were too large for his body, and his disjointed movements gave him a comical air.

"He's not a bull!" I cried. "Look at him! He's more like a Great Dane!"

But nobody paid any attention to me. They liked the other name better. It was based not only on his appearance but his demeanor: his wild enthusiasm for following the ball; his bewildered look when he found it in his hands; his immense seriousness, which combined the fighting bull's fearlessness with its ineffectiveness as it charges the red cape in the belief that it is the man, and is deceived over and over again, only to turn and attack once more with renewed fury, never learning to make for the bullfighter instead of the square of cloth.

In those days I was thin and frail, and knew absolutely nothing about basketball; I was sure no one would choose me for his team. I was surprised and delighted to find that I was mistaken. The two captains, the Rooster and Aréchiga, made their choices so that the sides would be evenly matched; first they selected the best players, then the mediocre ones, and finally the weakest. I was Aréchiga's last choice. Since we couldn't all play, several boys were left as spectators. I was very grateful to him for this, and I think the liking I always had for him was based on that kindness at our first meeting.

My joining the Y.M.C.A. was really the Bull's doing. Somewhere I had heard or read that muscular development hindered the intellect. Since I was physically weak, I was naturally seduced by the assertions that athletes were all imbeciles, that sports were a waste of time that might better be spent in reading or meditation, and that muscles were no longer of any use even for self-defense in an age when the weakling could resort to that great leveler, the pistol.

"That's not true," he told me. This was the expression he always used in our arguments; he never descended to saying "Don't be stupid," or "What an idiotic thing to say," as most of us Preparatory students did in heated discussions. "When I was in school in California," he went on, "a lot of the best students were good athletes. Everybody goes in for sports there, from the time they're little kids, and you should see what physiques they have. My health has always been delicate; when I was younger they wouldn't let me take any exercise because they thought I had tuberculosis. But I'm better now, and I want to develop some 'stamina.' That's what they call it at the Y. Besides," he added, showing a grasp of certain realities, "it's really cheap. With what you spend for your Sunday steam bath, which you say you like so much, you could pay the dues and have a bath every day, use the gym, play basketball, and swim." It was the last item that convinced me. Swimming was the only sport I was good at; that and riding were two things my father had taught us. I was eager to become an excellent swimmer.

Having made up my mind, I began to arrange for my enrollment in the Young Men's Christian Association; but I was surprised to find that my father was against it. When I told him of my plan, he made no attempt to hide his displeasure. The Y.M.C.A. was merely a front for Protestant propaganda. As I knew, he was far from being a rabid Catholic; he was not even very devout, and never went to mass. But Protestantism turned his stomach. I was old enough to make my own decisions, but he would never contribute a centavo to the support of those people who wanted to make a gringo out of me. His granting me the freedom of choice was, I realized, one more manifestation of his genuine liberalism. I decided to take advantage of it.

"All right," I said. "As long as you don't forbid it I'll join the Y." I pronounced it *Guay,* and he winced as though he had been slapped. "All I ask is that you keep on giving me my usual allowance for my Sunday steam baths."

My father had no objection to this. So, thanks to the Bull, I began to take part in sports—a passion that was to endure for the rest of my life.

This new interest was a natural reaction. When I compared my frail body with those of the boys who attended gym classes or played basketball, I firmly resolved to grow up to be a man with broad shoulders and well-developed biceps. It was a goal I never attained; but in the process of trying I learned many things that were decidedly more important. One of these was that there must be an equilibrium between mental and physical activity. This discovery changed my whole attitude toward life. During puberty I aspired to be a genius, to dazzle people with my remarkable intelligence, even at the cost of a miserable body and precarious health. This ambition was now forgotten. I became fascinated with the idea of a symmetrical development, and in order to build myself up physically began taking part in all sports. From then on my ideal was the complete personality—which, obviously, I didn't attain either. But sports taught me how to lose, how to bear physical pain without whining, and how to enjoy triumph— which is always ephemeral—without arrogance.

To say that the Bull was intelligent—extraordinarily so—does not give an accurate picture of him. The most outstanding quality of his mind was his "scientific" attitude toward any problem. He had a remarkable talent for comprehending and explaining physical phenomena, which constantly preoccupied him. He found these so simple and logical that he could never understand how other people could think they were difficult or complicated.

It isn't always easy to know the basic reasons for a friendship. In the case of the Bull and myself it might be explained by the fact that we were totally unlike. I was strongly attracted to this lad who would rather read a dull physics text than go to the movies; it struck me as absurd and at the same time admirable. The physical sciences were, and always have been, dry and boring to me. Consequently I admired any one who not only understood them easily but enjoyed talking about them.

The Bull was always trying to apply the scientific rigor of his favorite subjects to the events of everyday life. He would analyze the most trivial matters with all the method and order of an academic dissertation or a mathematical proof. In an adult this could have been annoyingly pedantic; in a boy just emerging from puberty it was sometimes extremely funny. And yet he did it so naturally, with such an absolute lack of conceit, taking it so for granted there was no other way to go about it, that you found yourself listening with real enjoyment. You were so fascinated by the logical development of his exposition that you forgot whether or not the subject under discussion was of any real importance.

One afternoon after literature class when we were walking to his house, where we had fallen into the habit of having a snack together, the question of the definition of fiction came up. For him, only truth was to be admired. He lamented the fact that in history and in the social sciences, which dealt with the complex factors of social phenomena, truth was so relative as to be almost undiscoverable. This was why, he said, he was not attracted by these subjects; they were not really sciences in the sense that physics and mathematics were. But he at least respected the efforts of those who were sincerely looking for truth in these fields. Making up stories and tales, relating things that had never taken place, on the other hand, was to him an unjustifiable waste of time. This kind of thing was all very well to amuse little children, but it was not suitable for adults. Grownups could spend their time better and certainly more agreeably by studying nature, or the functions of the human organism, or the construction of the universe, or by contemplating the marvelous and inexhaustible relationships that existed among numbers and could be expressed by orderly mathematical formulas. The implied conclusion was, of course, that the literature class was an unnecessary nuisance whose only apparent result was that it made its students pretentious.

His thesis struck me as so absurd that I took issue at once, with all the vehemence of my impulsive nature. I was offended by this contempt for my favorite subject. The Bull heard me out calmly, without betraying the least impatience—even when I dealt in insulting terms with people who were too insensitive or ignorant to appreciate works of literature. I grasped at every argument that came to my mind. I pointed out that in a literary work there is often to be found a more profound truth than in the simple observation of a physical phenomenon, for it expresses the state of mind, aspirations, or yearnings of the author—and in many cases actual events from his own life—thinly disguised by his imagination.

"The truth of the mind is truth, too," I said, with the conceited confidence of one who has begun to glean certain expressions from simple psychology books. "It may be a subjective truth, but that doesn't mean it's any less valid. Besides, it's made up of fragments of other realities: nobody can imagine anything that doesn't exist. There is nothing in the mind that has not entered through the senses," I concluded pedantically.

At the moment I couldn't recall where or when I had read these words, but as I repeated them I believed them to be my own and felt that their argument was incontrovertible. The Bull answered me in a very low voice, as though he were talking to himself; I could hardly hear him above the noise of the streetcars and automobiles on Bolívar Street. What he said astounded me.

"Truth is the relationship that exists between our notions of things and the things themselves. The truth you're talking about is something I don't understand at all. The truth is that which exists, as somebody said. I think it was St. Augustine."

It was my turn not to understand. I had never read St. Augustine, and I didn't see how my friend, at fifteen, could possibly have read him. I was incapable of comprehending the immense profundity of that apparently simple statement. It was obvious that I would have to beat him on less slippery ground. I changed my tactics.

"Literature teaches us to express ourselves properly, and you can't deny that we should know how to do that," I said, ignoring his last statement. I was pleased at having found an argument that by implication criticized my adversary for his defects and peculiarities of speech—which he was the first to deplore. I coolly waited for his answer.

"I have nothing against studying grammar," he replied unhurriedly. "I remember a teacher in Cuba who used to say that he intended to instruct us in the art of speaking elegantly. It struck me oddly that he should say that when he spoke so badly himself. But when I began to read the textbook I saw that he wasn't referring to pronunciation but to a knowledge of the language. I realized that it was quite possible for him to know Spanish very well and yet say *fóforo* for *fósforos*. But aren't you confusing literature with grammar?"

Without waiting for a reply, he went on with the air of someone making an effort to remember. "Grammar is the set of rules . . ." He recited the definition we had learned in class. "That's very good. Grammar is fascinating. It analyzes language and shows us its inner workings, which are surprisingly logical. Did you ever stop to think about the strange harmony in verbs—especially the irregular ones? When I first learned them I thought they were absurd; but I soon saw that I was wrong. They are filled with rhythm and harmony. Just think how monotonous a language would be if all its verbs were regular."

I had no answer prepared, so I thought it best to say nothing. The subject seemed to interest him, and he went on talking about language as though it were something he had thought about a great deal. He was still on the irregular verbs.

"They're like the variations on a theme in a symphony. You expect to hear the theme again in a little while, and sure enough, there it comes. But it isn't quite the same. It's that slight variation that adds to its beauty. The theme itself is made more powerful by the modification."

I had heard a few symphonies in the Preparatory amphitheater on school holidays, when the Conservatory orchestra had played between speeches; but I had never traced a theme, much less a variation. I found myself in a very weak position in this argument.

I was discouraged at hearing the Bull talk so easily about

matters on which I was completely ignorant, and which did not at all square with my estimate of him. That he should know about physics was all very well; that he should like mathematics—good for him! But I couldn't tolerate the fact that he was also familiar with music and could quote St. Augustine—all for the love of truth and in the defense of a thesis that was notoriously false. I let him go on as long as he liked, hardly following his argument as I searched my mind for a reply.

We were almost at his house when I took advantage of a pause to say, "Don't get off the subject. I say that literature teaches us to speak correctly, and that it does it in the best possible way: by example. What good are all those rules and all those observations of yours about verbal harmony if you can't apply them in a natural and spontaneous way? This is what good books are for. Not to mention an even more important purpose, which is to give us pleasure."

I was pleased with myself. I felt that I had not only brought forth a very sound argument, but that I had expressed it extremely well.

"Look. All that talk about pleasure doesn't impress me. I don't even like the word. It makes me think of sexual enjoyment. You must have picked it up from one of those novels you find so instructive. And yet you may be right, basically. I think it might be a good idea for me to read some literature. It would probably do me good."

With these words we parted. As I walked home I felt quite pleased that my friend had seen my point of view. Something within me was proud at the thought that I could influence his life and set him on a path that I felt was a more human one. I reviewed my arguments, and tried to think of others I had overlooked.

Thus began our long, never-ending discussions. They were usually heated on my side and calm on his, but they were always amicable. At the end one of us would always concede with good grace that the other was right.

The following day in geography, while the teacher was preparing to call the roll, my friend told me, "I've decided which book I'm going to start with: *Don Quixote*. I suppose you approve?"

I nodded my head, for the class was silent now. I was flattered, although I was sure the Bull would never get past the first chapter. Once again I was wrong. My friend was to read some of Cervantes' book almost every night in his life. In those days, usually his mother read it aloud to him. These reading sessions were typical of the total understanding that existed between them. I have seen many affectionate mothers and many obedient sons; but never have I witnessed such companionship, such comradery, between a mother of some thirty-odd years and a boy in his teens.

Eduardo's mother was his advisor, confidante, and never-failing partner in conversation. She listened with genuine interest to his long dissertations on scientific matters and his questions about the books he was reading. She played games with him, and was his efficient and valued assistant in his laboratory, where he spent many hours amid test tubes and electric wires. These activities could not be classified as study or amusement; there was something of both in them, but for him they were clearly and simply fun. I learned later, however, that he was doing serious and systematic research, especially in the field of electricity, in that improvised laboratory.

I was admitted to the sanctum sanctorum one day. To me it was all a meaningless jumble. One corner was occupied by small transformers, coils, and other electrical apparatus, while the other was filled with test tubes, mortars, filter paper, and miscellaneous chemical equipment I had never seen before. The Bull showed me these things, which were obviously very precious to him, one by one, and explained what they were for and how they were used. They were the toys and playmates of an only child who was always alone, without brothers or sisters or friends.

His only friend was, as I said, his mother. His father, who was from Cádiz, was by inclination an amateur painter, and by necessity a traveling salesman. Don Carlos was a little man, totally bald, with a salt-and-pepper Vandyke. He adored his wife, who was almost thirty years younger than he, and for her sake had given up painting and had gone into business; he traveled all over the Republic, selling anything he could. Like most Andalusians, he was violent by nature and given to the wildest kind of exaggeration in his speech. His temperament was just the opposite of his son's, whom he idolized but could not understand. The Bull, with all the egoism of a spoiled child, made not the slightest effort to comprehend his father, and detested everything in which he took pleasure: art in general, painting, and particularly poetry. Don Carlos loved writing verses and reading them aloud, which couldn't have humiliated Eduardo more. This may have been the reason for the boy's pronounced distaste for literature, which had occasioned our first argument.

And so, without brothers, sisters, friends, or an understanding father, the Bull had taken whole-hearted refuge in the love and sympathy of his mother. She had responded by adapting herself in an extraordinary way to her son's tastes. When Eduardo bought his first automobile, for example—it was a second-hand Oakland that cost him six hundred pesos—Doña María Ángeles became a mechanic's helper. With infinite patience and a rare, genuine, and contagious cheerfulness, the Señora would spend all Sunday

morning seated on the ground beside the automobile, from under which projected her son's skinny legs and his enormous, incongruous feet.

The car was on its last legs when he bought it; he insisted on overhauling it so that (he said) they could go out for Sunday afternoon drives. This was merely a pretext. He never had any intention of driving the vehicle. Like a child with a new toy, he merely wanted to see what was inside and how it was put together. He spent hours taking apart and reassembling various parts of it, finding out how they worked. So usually when afternoon came the car was more out of order than in the morning, and mother and son were so exhausted that going for a drive was out of the question anyway. They would spend the rest of the day reading.

One Sunday morning when I called to invite him to come with me to watch the girls coming out of twelve-o'clock mass, I was met by the scene I have described above: the automobile all apart, Doña María seated oriental fashion on the cement driveway amid replacement parts, and the Bull's huge feet sticking out from underneath.

He crawled out to greet me, covered with grease.

"Have you ever seen what an ingenious thing a carburetor is?"

He held out both hands full of little parts that looked to me like pieces of an alarm clock.

"Really ingenious, and yet very simple," he said.

I had no doubt that the first was true; but it didn't appear at all simple to me. On the contrary, I was sure that I couldn't even have tried to put that apparatus together again. When I told him so he smiled in a pleased way. It gratified him to see my respect for his cleverness in matters that I was totally unable to comprehend.

"It's easy, really. You can do it yourself. Put on these 'overalls' "
—he used the English word—"so you won't get your clothes dirty,
and we'll get to work."

Following his orders, I soon found myself cleaning a little very
fine wire screen with gasoline; at first I thought it was a piece of
felt, and then I learned that it was the fuel filter, clogged with
dirt. With his help, I began putting the carburetor together. When
we finished it was time for lunch. Sunday morning had gone by
before we knew it, and although I regretted having missed our
DonJuanesque expedition, I was pleased that I had mastered such
a complex device. My friend invited me to have lunch with them.
I hadn't intended to stay, but I accepted gladly on the condition
that we take the car out for a trial spin afterward; I was curious
to see if the carburetor that I had helped to assemble was really
going to work.

When I entered the dining room, the whole family was there:
the Bull, his parents, and his grandmother. His mother had slipped
away to wash and change while we were still engrossed in our
mechanical chores, and for the first time I realized what a beautiful face she had. She was the classic beauty from Madrid, celebrated in so many songs: olive skin, large black eyes, black hair
that waved slightly, a rather wide mouth with full lips and a frank,
easy smile, and a clear, noble forehead. There was great intelligence there, at times mixed with a curious sadness. She was inclined to be fat, and at thirty-five had lost her youthful figure;
but in spite of her weight she moved gracefully. Her outstanding
characteristic was her continual good humor, her never-failing
cheerfulness. In this respect the contrast between her and her
husband was striking; for while she always saw the good side of
everything, whatever was kind and noble and bright, he was bitter
and gloomy and inclined to see only the worst aspects of things.

He took everything seriously, but nothing seemed to bother her. "What's the point of getting all worked up?" she would demand with that Madrid accent of hers.

As I came to know her better I appreciated more and more her remarkable good sense and her high degree of intelligence. She had the rare talent of being able to give sensible advice in complex matters; she could cut through the clutter of details and impertinent facts and arrive at the basic issue. She said it was simply intuition, and perhaps she was right; for whenever she spoke it was as though there were centuries of a whole nation's experience behind her, rather than as if she had discovered the solution for herself after a laborious analysis of the problem.

Sunsets

He was buried in the Dolores cemetery, under a very modest stone bearing the dates of his birth and death, indistinguishable from the others about it. His monument was like the man himself, who was never able to rise above his surroundings. His funeral, on the other hand, by one of life's bitter ironies, was most sumptuous.

My father had been laid out in the center of my brother's ample parlor, surrounded by four huge candles. As I watched the flickering flames and the patterns of light and shadow on the faces of the guests who had come to attend the wake, the story of his life passed through my mind. What a contrast between this scene, with its hundreds of visitors milling about through the house, hardly able to get in or out, or standing in line to pay their respects, and his own career, which was so uneventful, so devoid of triumph, so lacking in real friendship!

The house was jammed. Some of the guests were chatting in adjoining rooms; others were leaning in doorways and stealing furtive glances at their watches, waiting for the moment when they could slip away unobserved.

In that moving stream of humanity were some of the most distinguished personages in politics, industry, diplomacy, art, education, and government; and yet when the American ambassador appeared, he stood out at once. Josephus Daniels was unmistakable. He had the good-natured face of a healthy child, and wore a huge black bow tie and carried the black hat of an old-time "Southern gentleman." He was a likable and cheerful man who insisted on repeating over and over again the four words of Spanish he knew. Although he was at bottom very American, his presence and impeccable manners distinguished him from most of his compatriots; he was as far from being a typical "businessman" as a duke of the most ancient Italian lineage would be. He came with his secretary, a Spaniard who went with him everywhere and served as his interpreter. After fifteen minutes, which he considered the proper amount of time according to protocol, he left, distributing discreet smiles and handshakes.

Toward nine in the evening there was another stir when the Secretary of Defense arrived. By that time it was common knowledge that he would be the Republic's next president, and everyone hastened to make way for him with a smile. General Manuel Ávila Camacho was an affable and yet serious man, one of those people one likes at first sight. He greeted his friends and took a chair in one corner of the room, where soon a small crowd gathered about him. They spoke so softly I couldn't hear all they were saying; but from the General's expression and the occasional word that reached me I gathered that the subject was one of no great importance: horse breeding, perhaps. Even so, his audience paid such rapt attention to his every word that one would have thought they were listening to something unheard-of and marvelous. How true it is, I thought, that the people who surround political figures will go to any lengths to flatter them; they will make them believe that their every utterance is interesting, clever, profound, or extraordinary—according to what the interested party happens to want. And then one day the public official is at last convinced that he belongs to a race apart, endowed with every physical and moral virtue, and that he is an exceptional and superior human being who is incapable of error!

As time went by and guests kept arriving, the gathering began to look more like a party, as if the people attending had forgotten that they were at a wake. A group in the dining room, under the influence of the coffee and the brandy, were passing the time pleasantly by telling dirty stories and laughing more and more loudly. The truly afflicted members of the family, overcome by grief or exhaustion, found dark corners where they could doze quietly unobserved—the women under cover of their black shawls, the men with their faces hidden in their hands.

It was quite late when the President of the Republic arrived with two members of his cabinet. General Lázaro Cárdenas wore a grave expression, in which were mingled dignity and sorrow. He nodded to the guests and then looked around the room for my brother and myself; when he found us he came over and gave us both an abrazo of condolence. It was not one of those stingy, half-hearted embraces with just one arm, but his usual effusive hug with a great deal of pounding on the back. After a few moments of silence he asked to be allowed to stand the last vigil with us, and left. With his innate sense of tact he managed to give an impression of easiness and affection that belied his high position, although he had not uttered more than a couple of words and had not stayed any longer than absolutely necessary. One of his ministers left with him; the other, who perhaps felt more like a friend of the family, remained all night. He was a good conversationalist, exceptionally well informed on national and international affairs, and loved late hours; it was no hardship for him to talk almost without interruption until dawn.

When the sun came up there was no one left but the closest relatives and a few of their friends. In the daylight their faces looked pale, and the gardenias were yellow and ugly against their background of purple wreaths. The house was in disorder, and the servants added to the confusion as they came and went with coffee for those who had been there all night. It looked like the aftermath of a party. This impression was incongruous in view of the casket and the candles, which were now nearly consumed; their flames seemed dim and yellow in the sunlight that came in through the half-closed curtains.

It was time for the last vigil. My brother and I stood on either side in front of the casket; behind it were General Ávila Camacho, who had returned a few moments before, and the President's private secretary, whom he had sent to represent him. Beyond them stood a justice of the Supreme Court and a Cabinet member. The wake no longer seemed like a family affair; it looked more like an official ceremony.

During the brief moments of the vigil, all the previous night's weariness and grief came back to me. I felt a great misery, which was more physical than emotional; my eyes burned, and tears ran down my cheeks and over my lips, but I didn't even know I was crying. I had gone without sleep for several nights while my father was slowly dying; I had had to greet guests while trying to maintain the resigned and mournful attitude that was expected of me —although there had been moments when I didn't feel at all resigned, and others when I had forgotten all about my sorrow. All this had made me feel like a hypocrite, and the effort it had required had exhausted me even more.

When we concluded our vigil, all of us picked up the coffin and put it into the hearse that was standing at the front door. Then we got into the automobiles, and the procession began. The line of cars seemed endless; I have no idea how many there were. The long cortege moved slowly up one street and down another. We crossed Colonia del Valle, went up Insurgentes to Tacubaya, and from there continued at a snail's pace to the Dolores cemetery.

When the cemetery came in sight I suddenly became aware that something within me had changed during the silent ride. The grief I felt at my father's death had inexplicably been relegated to second place, and another, more distant sorrow had reawakened. My mother's death, with the anguish I had almost forgotten, came back to me.

Through some strange associative process I saw again the scenes that had remained hidden in my subconscious for twenty-five years. Was it because of the contrast between the two funerals? Was it, perhaps, that I felt somehow that she had been treated unfairly? As though the exterior appearance of things could affect their content, this lavish funeral of my father's, in which there was possibly a great deal of hypocrisy, had in fact mitigated my grief; my mother's, so undignified and pitiful, struck me now as shameful as I recalled it in all its sordidness.

I don't know exactly when her illness began. One of my

earliest memories is the sound of my own childish voice repeating the same formula every night before going to bed: "Good night, mamá, I hope you feel better tomorrow." I can't recall ever having seen my mother healthy and smiling. I knew in a vague way that something was wrong with her heart. Our maids gave me to understand that her illness had been brought on by the many sorrows in her life.

When we first moved to Azcapotzalco I was confident that the change from the city to the country would contribute to her recovery. That old idea about the pure air and the peace and quiet that are supposed to exist outside the city! But it didn't turn out that way. From her armchair, where she spent her days in silence, never complaining but always sunk in deep melancholy, she was carried to her bed, where her face seemed even more pallid against the whiteness of the sheets. We were in the middle of the Tragic Ten Days* at the time, and in some way that isn't very clear I associated the worsening of her disease with the prevalent anxiety throughout the country and the state of alarm due to the fighting in Mexico City.

By listening to her doctors I learned the name of her disease and something of its nature. It was a malfunctioning of one of the valves of the heart, known as "mitral insufficiency." To my ear the term carried a strange religious connotation—perhaps because I associated it with a bishop's miter—and I regarded her illness as an ineluctable evil that had been sent from "on high." It was incurable; but I was not aware of that, nor did it ever

---

* February 9–18, 1913, when General Victoriano Huerta, ostensibly putting down a revolt of Díaz supporters, imprisoned President Francisco I. Madero and Vice-President José María Pino Suárez and forced the congress to name him president. On February 22 he had Madero and Pino Suárez shot. *Tr.*

occur to me that my mother might die. She was an integral part of my life, an inherent element in the milieu in which I was growing up. She was indispensable and irreplaceable. I assumed that hers was a passing disease, like the ones I had had—measles or chicken pox or scarlet fever. These were things you had to live through, but then they went away and you forgot about them. Her symptoms were not the same, but I didn't see that that made any difference. She had no fever, but complained of a persistent, indefinite "sick" feeling, of fatigue, of swollen feet; and she was unable to take an interest in anything about her. Maybe she would always be ill; some older people were like that. (I thought of my mother as an old woman, although she was not yet forty.)

Only once did it occur to me that she might be seriously ill. That was the day they moved her to the hospital. I asked my brother if he thought our mother was really sick enough to have to go to that horrible place; with the protective attitude he always had toward me, he tried to reassure me. No, it was nothing to worry about. It was just that at home we lacked some of the conveniences she needed. "Look, we don't even have a bathroom. They can look after her better in the hospital." I was easily convinced, although I could feel that he regarded the hospital with the same horror as I and all Mexicans did in those days.

I went there to see her one morning, as I did every day when I didn't have classes. I was feeling especially happy that day, for no reason except that I was young and in good health, and the weather was glorious. At that early hour the carefully kept gardens of the old Regina Hospital were fragrant with newly opened roses and damp earth; and the ancient building had just been cleaned and no longer looked so forbidding. The rosebushes were shaped like little trees, and I wondered if they grew that way naturally or had been pruned to look like that. I decided to try trimming the two or three that grew in our garden to see if they would produce big blooms like these that were sparkling with morning dew. I liked the little shell-shaped plants that edged the flower beds, too; they lent a formal look to the garden. They were round and light green, all alike and evenly spaced; they fascinated me— especially the older ones that had begun to climb over the red brick borders. Tiny offspring were creeping out from under some of them, climbing over each other like new-born puppies crowding about their mother's teats.

I went along happily thinking about these things, skipping over the big, square red tiles on the floor of the hospital corridor. I had made up a kind of game in which I was not allowed to step on the cracks, and this made me take strides of different lengths, almost like ballet steps. When I came to Room 8 the door was open and there was no one there. The bed was neatly made. As all the rooms looked alike, I thought perhaps it was not the same one where I had left my mother the night before. I went back to look at the number. No, it was number eight, all right. I didn't know what to think. Had they changed her room? I waited until one of the nurses, who were nuns, came by in her starched white headdress. It gave her such a formal and immaculate look that I hardly dared approach her. At last I gathered the courage to ask in a timid voice, "Where did they take my mamá?"

The nun stood looking at me in an odd way for a moment, as though she were surprised by my question and were trying to guess how much I knew.

"She's downstairs," she said.

I didn't move or give any indication that I understood what she meant. I suppose she finally decided that I had been told.

"They took her away early this morning. We lost her during the night."

I understood the words, but they meant nothing to me. I remained standing there. The nun awakened me from my stupor.

"Come with me."

Together we went down the wide, dark stairway. We stopped at a door like all the rest on the first floor. She opened it, crossed herself on the threshold, and went in soundlessly. I followed her. There, on an ordinary hospital cot, completely covered with a sheet, lay the person I knew to be my mother. It was a small, bare room with white walls, adorned only with a crucifix over the head of the bed. There were four candles burning. Although there could no longer be any doubt that my mother was dead, I somehow felt like an unconcerned spectator. A few wisps of her blond hair had escaped from under the sheet, and in the flickering candlelight seemed to move as though they were still alive. There was absolute silence, and a smell of disinfectant. There were no flowers. I felt as if I were in a vacuum. I turned to speak to the nun, but she was gone.

I had heard or read somewhere—I'm sure I had never seen it —that bereaved children, mad with grief, threw themselves desperately on the cadavers of their parents, as though refusing to let them go. I must confess that I did no such thing. What I felt was fear. Now that I had been left alone with the body in that small, closed room, I wanted only to get out of there. I don't know exactly why, but I was filled with a physical terror, a genuine panic. It may have been that superstitious fear that is so stupidly inculcated in us from childhood, or possibly merely awe in the presence of death. I don't know. Convinced that it was wicked of me not to be grief-stricken, I kept telling myself that "that thing" on the bed was my mother, my dead mother. But I didn't believe it. I felt only repugnance for that corpse, and for the odor it gave off, that mingled with the smell of burning wax and the disin-

fectant I could almost taste in my mouth—repugnance for that bare room and everything in it. It was an unconquerable horror, and finally I fled before it. Filled with shame, I sneaked away like a criminal and hid myself in the garden, searching for the smell of damp earth, newly opened roses, and freshly watered plants that I had so enjoyed when I first arrived. But there was no longer any perfume there for me; all my senses were blocked by that feeling of shame, as though I had dishonorably deserted my post.

I tried to rationalize what I had done by telling myself that what I had seen there on the cot was no longer my mother, that she had died and gone somewhere else. But the words did not convince me. I whispered to myself sadly and hopefully, "It's because I'm not a man yet. I'll be brave when I grow up." I was sure that it was my duty to return to the funeral chapel and stay with the body; but something stronger than myself wouldn't let me.

I wandered along the red dirt paths in that meticulously tended garden for some time, then at last slowly approached the main entrance of the building. I still wanted to run away, but I felt that I should keep my eye on the door of the room where my mother was. I waited anxiously for someone to come. Fortunately my Aunt Carlota showed up shortly with her daughter Rosaura. The moment I saw my aunt I ran to her, threw myself into her arms, and for the first time was able to cry. She did her best to console me, but her very presence was more comfort than any words: now I knew I would not be alone. Gradually I grew calmer. Then my father arrived, looking grave. He came up to us without a word, in that quick, rhythmic, swinging gait of his I knew so well. I kissed his hand, as was our custom when we met, and he put his hand on my head and led me toward the mortuary. I didn't want to go with him, but I could think of no way to get out of it. At any rate, I wouldn't be all by myself this time. When we entered the room and my father saw that there was no one with the body, he turned to me and said gently, with a slight tone of reprimand, "You shouldn't have left her alone." I didn't dare confess what I had felt, and said nothing. He went up to the bed and stood silently regarding his wife. His eyes filled with tears, and his lower lip trembled. I had never seen him cry; it made him look like a child, and not at all like my father.

After a moment he took a small pair of scissors from his pocket and slowly, like someone carrying out a solemn rite, cut a lock of hair from the dead woman's head. He put it carefully in a little envelope and returned it with the scissors to his pocket. Then he leaned over and kissed her on the forehead. Turning to me, he said, "Kiss her good-by." I conquered my revulsion enough to put my lips against that terribly white brow; but at the touch of the cold, damp skin I shuddered, lost control, and bolted from the room.

No one seemed to notice my misery; but I was disgusted with myself for what I felt were my improper feelings, and persisted in a hopeless attempt to justify them. I told myself that my mother had gone away, that she no longer inhabited that body, that it was only an empty husk. Hadn't I heard people referring to corpses that way? It was no more than a handful of dust, something left behind when the soul departed. But I couldn't convince myself. I went on feeling ashamed and humiliated, reproaching myself for being different, as I thought, from other people. Why couldn't I show filial love like everybody else? Miserable, I took refuge again in the garden and hid behind the plants. I was roused from my soliloquy by the voices of my father and aunt, who were coming in my direction; the subject of conversation was a disagreeable one, judging from their tone. It appeared that my father had no money to pay for the wake and the burial, and was trying to think of some solution to the problem. As they came nearer I heard him say, "I'll get the money to bury her, even if I have to steal it."

Although this didn't sound like a solution to me, they seemed to think it was, for they didn't refer to it again, and went on to discuss the matter of the wake. My father pointed out that moving the body to our house in Coachilco, on the other side of Azcapotzalco, would not only add to the expense but make it very inconvenient for those who wanted to be with her that night. The house was too small to hold all our family and friends, not to mention the fact that would be hard to find at night, for there were no street lights. There was something more he didn't dare to say, but which was implied in his tone of voice. I could see that he was hesitating, saying the same thing over and over again, waiting for something. He was holding back, as though hoping for some reaction from his sister-in-law. I guessed what it was: an offer that was not forthcoming. At last he took courage and put it into words: would she mind if they held the wake at her house, since it was larger and not so far away? He didn't say as much, but he implied: "After all, she's your sister." My aunt hesitated.

"Look," she said at last. "I'll be frank with you. I'd like to, but..."

She didn't finish her sentence, but there was no need to. My father's only answer was that gesture of his that meant: "Nothing we can do about it!" It involved the body as much as the face: his shoulders shot up and his lower lip folded down. He turned his back on her, chucked me under the chin, and said, "There will be no wake for your mother. We'll have to take her to the mortuary." He quickly walked away, without saying good-by. My aunt turned to her daughter and said, almost as though she were talking to herself but loudly enough for me to hear, "God only knows what kind of friends he would have brought into our house." Rosaura agreed: "I'll bet some of them would even be Masons." This seemed to satisfy my aunt that she had done the right thing.

I didn't understand the word "mortuary," but I knew that there would be no wake, and I was glad. The idea of spending the night with the body, receiving condolences, hearing the same words over and over, and making the same replies filled me with horror. I was sure that it would only make me more and more miserable. And yet when the time came to take my mother to the mortuary, and I saw what it meant, I was even further depressed by the sordidness of it all.

This took place that same afternoon, at the Dolores cemetery. Half a dozen people, besides my father, my brother, and I, followed the men from the Gayosso funeral agency who carried the coffin. We entered a building that seemed terribly dark after the brilliant sunshine outside. We proceeded to a compartment in the wall, into which the men shoved the coffin unceremoniously. They wiped the sweat from their faces and left immediately without a word, not even waiting for a tip; they had finished an unpleasant job, and knew they were dealing with poor people. After a moment of indecision, we followed them out the door. My father came up to my brother and myself and explained: "She'll be buried tomorrow. It would be better if you two didn't come." We nodded and exchanged a knowing look.

Outside, we began walking faster, as though all of us were anxious to leave the cemetery. We went along with bowed heads and no one said a word. I felt sick and cold inside, as though that lonely, squalid place where my mother's body would remain overnight had left its chill in my bones. Now I knew what they meant by "taking her to the mortuary." It meant abandoning her, leaving her all by herself in a gloomy place, with none of the attention and respect we all owed her. It was as though we had never loved her, almost as if her remains had been an unclaimed corpse in the morgue.

My remorse returned. Wasn't this the same as I had done that morning, when I had run out of the room where she was lying? Or was this even worse, since we were all doing it together? We were a group, without even the justification I had had: we had no reason to be afraid. Then why were we doing this? Because some of us were improvident and the rest were selfish. Not only was I angry, but a physical pain rose from my stomach and crowded about my heart. The unconsoling tears streamed down my face. My throat was tight, and I wanted to scream. Now, for the first time, I fully understood what I had lost. This was what death was: absolute, irremediable, eternal separation.

Night was falling. In the distance we could barely make out the edge of Chapultepec Park. We boarded the little mule-drawn streetcar that ran from the cemetery to Tacubaya. The driver turned the crank on the right side of his platform that unrolled a chain and released the brakes. He flicked the reins over the animals' backs, gave a command, and the little car went down the hill toward the first houses of Tacubaya.

The red glow of sunset was rapidly disappearing from the sky. I felt that the afternoon had died, and that with it, and with my mother, my childhood had died also.